HUDSON'S

Guide to Historic Properties in

Scotland

1997

The entrance hall at Fyvie Castle, Aberdeenshire, Grampian.

Scotland

Scotland's geographical background ...

Kilchurn Castle, Loch Awe, Argyll (West Highlands).

Andy Williams

Culzean Castle, Ayrshire (South of Scotland).

Cawdor Castle, Nairn (The Highlands).

Area

Scotland is a country of some 30,414 square miles (78,772 square kilometres) in area, just over one-third of the total area of Great Britain.

Weather

Scotland's position on the edge of Europe, surrounded by sea on three sides, means its weather is very varied. Although Scotland is on the path of prevailing south westerly, rain-bearing winds from the Atlantic, several East Coast resorts have annual rainfall less than that of Rome (29.5", 749mm). May and June are usually drier than July and August. Many popular destinations, such as Nairn near Inverness, Kelso in the Scottish Borders, Ayr on the Clyde Coast, Dumfries in Galloway, Pitlochry in Perthshire, Braemar on Royal Deeside and several more have less rain on average than New York. In general, Scotland's East Coast tends to be cool and dry, the West Coast milder and wetter.

If there is rain, the ever changing weather patterns mean it will probably not last long and with Scotland's long daylight hours (the midsummer sun sets in Shetland at 2234hrs, an hour and a quarter after the official London time,) there is plenty of time to fit in a full sightseeing day.

Physical features

The greatest distance from north to south is 275 miles (440km) and from east to west 154 miles (248km); the distance between the Firths of Forth and Clyde in the Central Belt is only 25 miles (41km). However, so rugged and indented is the coastline of Scotland that its total length is estimated at 2,300 miles (3,680km). There are about 790 islands, of which 130 are inhabited. Mainland sea lochs number at least 40.

Mountains

Scotland is a mountainous country, with 279 distinct peaks over 3,000 ft (914m) and the highest peak in the UK (Ben Nevis 4,406ft or 1,356m). Peaks over 3,000ft are known as Munros, after the mountaineer who first classified them.

Natural Scotland

The higher slopes of the Scottish mountains are often refuges for rare arctic/alpine plants, while the hill country and moorland is home to the red deer, golden eagle and peregrine falcon. Wildcat favour the rocky terrain of the west, with red squirrel, capercailzie and pine marten to be found in the native pinewoods of the central Highlands.

Scotland supports some of the greatest concentrations of seabirds in the world – gannets, puffins, guillemots and kittiwakes – while seals are commonly seen in large numbers on the rocky coasts and islands.

The Scottish Nation

The name "Scotland" is derived from the Scoti, a Celtic tribe who migrated to Scotland from Ireland during the fifth and sixth centuries and in time merged through conquest and intermarriage with the Pictish tribes to form the nucleus of the Scottish nation.

Population

Total	5,100,000 (1991)
Glasgow	765,000 (approx)
Edinburgh	420,000
Aberdeen	215,000
Dundee	175,000
Inverness	40,000

About 75% of Scotland's population live in the Central Lowlands.

Contents

Scotland is divided into six main regions, plus the cities of Glasgow and Edinburgh, the capital.

Front cover picture: Kilchurn Castle, Loch Awe. Photograph: Andy Williams.

Information contained in this guide is believed to be correct at the time of printing. It is based on that supplied by owners of the various properties and every effort is made to ensure its accuracy. Nevertheless prices, opening times and events can be changed at the discretion of the owners. The publishers cannot be held responsible for any consequences that may arise from errors or omissions. If long journeys are involved visitors are advised to telephone the property to ensure the opening times are as published.

© Published by Norman Hudson & Company 1997.
High Wardington House, Upper Wardington, Banbury OX17 1SP.
Tel: 01295 750750. Fax: 01295 750800.
www.:http://there.is/hudsons

ISBN: 0 9514157 9 4

KEY TO SYMBOLS

General information

Catering/Functions
Catering available for special functions,
corporate hospitality, wedding receptions, etc.

Disabled
Suitability of property for
disabled visitors and any constraints.

Refreshments
Tearoom, café, restaurant information.

Guided Tours
Availability and requirements for groups, etc.

Parking
Availability for cars and coaches.
Also courier and group leader information.

Schools/Education
Special facilities for school visits or
educational needs which can be provided.

Dogs
Acceptability and any constraints.

Overnight Accommodation
Provision and any constraints.

All information published is supplied by owners of the properties.
Every effort is made to ensure that it is correct at time of publication.
Changes can occur. If long journeys or special requirements are involved,
visitors are advised to telephone the properties in advance.

Historic Houses Association Member,
offering access under HHA Friends Scheme.

Property owned by
The National Trust for Scotland.

Property in the care of Historic Scotland.

Thirlestane Castle, Berwickshire (South of Scotland).

Scotland

Scotland's history – a brief synopsis ...

Early History

Although evidence shows that the earliest known residents of Scotland established a settlement on the Argyll peninsula as long ago as 6000 BC, recorded history can be said to start around 79–80 AD. At this time a Roman army led by Agricola invaded in an effort to subdue the troublesome Pictish Caledonian tribes of the north. Failing to do so, they retreated to England.

By the year 500, newcomers from Ireland, a Celtic tribe identified as Scoti, launched a successful invasion from the west, establishing a clear ethnic pattern – Picts in the north, Scoti in the west, Britons in the south west, and Angles in the south east. The Scots and Britons were Christians, and in about 580 St Columba successfully converted the King of the Picts to Christianity.

However, there were many years of conflict before the Picts and Scots finally united in 844 under the rule of Kenneth MacAlpin, king of the Scots. The complete union of Scotland was eventually achieved under the rule of Malcolm II (1005–1034) when the four major tribes united.

Falkland Palace, Fife.

Sovereign Scotland

Certain dominant themes keep recurring in Scotland's rich and complicated story. First and foremost is the mistrust between Scotland and England that manifested itself in 700 years of intermittent warfare.

Secondly, in the 16th century there began a lengthy religious struggle between the Presbyterians and Roman Catholics.

John Knox (1505–72) became a dynamic reformer in the Presbyterian cause, arguing bitterly with the Catholic Mary Queen of Scots. He also played a leading role in making Scotland the most scholastically-minded country in the world. The (Presbyterian) Church of Scotland's position as the established Church was finally secured by the settlement of 1688.

A third major factor was the link forged between Scotland and Europe in matters of culture, commerce, war and politics. Most notable of these ties was the "Auld Alliance" with France, dating from 1295, when the Scots sought French help against an English invasion.

Unions of crown and parliament

Two important dates in Scotland are 1603 and 1707. The first marks the Union of the Crowns of Scotland and England, when James VI of Scotland, the son of Mary Queen of Scots, assumed the throne of England as James I. This was a first major step towards full political and Parliamentary union, which followed in 1707 through legislation uniting the English and Scottish Parliaments.

However, Scots did not take as easily to union. In 1689, the English Parliament stripped the Catholic James II of his crown and imported the Protestant monarchs William and Mary from Holland. The Jacobite cause (the name stems from Jacobus, the Latin form of James) then became the focal point for Scottish unrest. First the Old Pretender (the exiled king) and then his son Bonnie Prince Charlie tried to regain the British throne for the House of Stuart. Finally, the last Jacobite rebellion was crushed at the Battle of Culloden in 1746.

A new era

After the Jacobite rebellions, the Scots turned their talents to the ways of peace and truly remarkable results. Scottish genius seemed not so much to flower as to erupt.

Philosophers, writers, inventors, architects, engineers and men of science and medicine all seemed to reach the height of their powers in a brief span of two or three decades during the Age of Enlightenment.

The work of these gifted men had a radical impact on the Scottish economy. From about 1750 onwards, industry profited from the new creative spirit. Ironworks and factories were built, new coal mines sunk, and new shipyards opened. David and Robert Napier, founders of marine engineering, started the shipbuilding industry on the Clyde where later the great

Castle Fraser, Aberdeenshire.

Cunard liners were built. Scotland's "merchant navy" grew from an estimated 100 vessels in 1700 to more than 2,000 in 1800.

The country's population increased from an estimated 1,100,000 in 1707 to more than 1,600,000 by 1800. Art, literature, publishing and architecture flourished. Glasgow and Edinburgh became two of the most attractive cities in the United Kingdom, distinguished by elegant squares, streets and terraces, by stately civic buildings, and extensive parks. It was not long before Edinburgh was dubbed "the Athens of the North" while Glasgow became the second city of the British Empire, and indeed in 1938 hosted the great Empire Exhibition.

DUFF HOUSE
Banff

Duff House is one of the most imposing and palatial houses in Scotland, with a strong classical façade and a grand staircase leading to the main entrance. It remained in the hands of the Duffs, Dukes of Fife, until 1906 when the family presented the estate to Banff and Macduff, consigning its contents to the saleroom.

Since then it has had a colourful history as a hotel, sanatorium and prisoner-of-war camp, before being taken into the care of Historic Scotland in 1956 and after a comprehensive programme of structural repairs and extensive conservation and restoration, Duff House opened to the public as an outstation of the National Galleries of Scotland in April 1995.

Set in acres of parkland, by the banks of the River Deveron, Duff House is one of the glories of the North East. Designed by William Adam for William Duff (1st Earl Fife), it is dramatically sited next to the small fishing communities of Banff and Macduff and is a splendid example of Scottish Baroque architecture.

Drawn from the rich holdings of the National Galleries, highlights of the picture display include El Greco's St Jerome in Penitence, J G Cuyp's Dutch Family Group; and Allan Ramsay's magnificent full length portrait of Elizabeth Cunyngham has been transformed by recent cleaning, revealing a wonderfully subtle range of colours.

CONTACT

The Manager
Duff House
Banff
AB45 3SX
Tel: (01261) 818181
Fax: (01261) 818900

LOCATION

OS Ref. NT691 634

Banff. 47m NE of Aberdeen on A947

OPENING TIMES

SUMMER

1 April - 30 September
daily: 10am - 5pm.

WINTER

1 October - 31 March
Thur - Sun
10am - 5pm.

ADMISSION

Adult £3.00
Conc...................... £2.00
Family £6.50
Groups* (10+)......... £2.00

* per person.

Free admission to shop, tearoom, grounds and woodland walks.

Free wedding photography permitted in grounds. Wedding photography permitted in vestibule for fee of £50.

CONFERENCE/FUNCTION	
ROOM	MAX CAPACITY
Education Suite	100
Vestibule	65
Dining Room Salon	80
North Drawing Room	40

i Shop. Audio-visual room, baby changing facilities, playground, assault course, woodland walks. Croquet and French Boules equipment available for hire.

✕ Available for special functions, corporate hospitality, conferences.

♿ Access and parking, lift to gallery floor, wheelchairs. WC.

☕ Tearoom serving light lunches. Open: 10am - 5pm.

P Car and coach parking free, 4 coach spaces, coaches to book.

Schools admitted free, teachers' pack, education suite, teachers encouraged to pre-visit free.

ARBUTHNOTT HOUSE

Tel: 01561 361226 **Fax:** 01561 320476

Arbuthnott, Laurencekirk, Kincardineshire AB30 1PA

Owner: The Viscount of Arbuthnott **Contact:** The Master of Arbuthnott

Arbuthnott family home for 800 years with formal 17th century walled garden on unusually steep south facing slope. Well maintained grass terraces, herbaceous borders, shrubs and greenhouses.

Location: OS Ref. NO796 751. Off B967 between A90 and A92, 25m S of Aberdeen.

Opening Times: House: 4/5 & 25/26 May, 20/21 July, 3/4/ & 24/25 Aug: 2 - 5pm. Guided tours. Garden: All year, 9am - 5pm.

Admission: House: £3 Garden: £2.

🦽 Ground floor suitable. 🚶 Compulsory. 🅿 Ample. 🐕 No dogs.

BALFLUIG CASTLE

Tel: 0171 624 3200

Alford, Aberdeenshire AB33 8EJ

Owner: Mark Tennant of Balfluig **Contact:** Mark Tennant of Balfluig

Small 16th century tower house in farmland, restored in 1967.

Location: OS Ref. NJ586 151. Alford, Aberdeenshire.

Opening Times: By written appointment only to M I Tennant Esq, 30 Abbey Gardens, London NW8 9AT.

🦽 Not suitable. 🐕 No dogs.

BALMORAL CASTLE (GROUNDS & EXHIBITION)

Tel: 013397 42334

Balmoral, Ballater, Aberdeenshire AB35 5TB **Fax:** 013397 42471

Owner: HM The Queen **Contact:** Capt J R Wilson

Family holiday home of the Royal Family, bought by Prince Albert in 1852. Grounds and exhibition of paintings and works of art in the ballroom.

Location: OS Ref. NO256 951. Off A93 between Ballater and Braemar. 50m W of Aberdeen.

Opening Times: 1 May - 31 Jul: Mon - Sat, 10am - 5pm.

Admission: Adult £3, Child (under 16) Free, OAP £2.50.

🦽 House & grounds suitable. WC. ☕ Tearoom. 🐄 In grounds, on leads.

BALVENIE CASTLE

Tel: 01340 820121

Dufftown

Owner: Historic Scotland **Contact:** The Custodian

Picturesque ruins of 13th century moated stronghold originally owned by the Comyns. Visited by Edward I in 1304 and by Mary Queen of Scots in 1562. Occupied by Cumberland in 1746.

Location: OS Ref. NJ326 408. At Dufftown on A941.

Opening Times: 1 Apr - 30 Sept: Mon - Sat, 9.30am - 6.30pm, Sun, 2 - 6.30pm, last ticket 6pm.

Admission: Adult £1, Conc. 50p, Child 50p.

BRAEMAR CASTLE 🏛

Tel: 01339 741224

Braemar, Aberdeenshire AB5 4EX

Owner: Invercauld Estate **Contact:** J S Blackett

Turreted stronghold built in 1628 by the Earl of Mar and burnt by Farquharson of Inverey in 1689. Rebuilt in 1748 when garrisoned by Hanoverian troops. Now a fully furnished family residence.

Location: OS Ref. NO156 924. ½ m NE of Braemar on A93.

Opening Times: Easter - Oct: Sat - Thur, 10am - 6.pm.

Admission: Adult £2, OAP/Coach £1.50, Child £1.

ℹ️ Shop. 🦽 Not suitable. 🅿 Ample. 🐕 Guide dogs only.

Crathes Castle, Aberdeenshire.

BRODIE CASTLE

Douglas MacGregor

FORRES, MORAY IV36 0TE

Owner: *The National Trust for Scotland* ***Contact:*** *Dr Stephanie Blackden*

Tel: 01309 641371 **Fax:** 01309 641600

This imposing Castle stands in rich Morayshire parkland. The lime harled building is a typical 'Z' plan tower house with ornate corbelled battlements and bartizans, with 17th & 19th century additions. The interior has unusual plaster ceilings, a major art collection, porcelain and fine furniture. There is a woodland walk by a large pond with access to wildlife observation hides. In springtime the grounds are carpeted with many varieties of daffodils for which Brodie Castle is rightly famous.

Location: OS Ref. NH980 577. Off A96 4½ m W of Forres and 24m E of Inverness.

Opening Times: Castle: Good Fri - 30 Sept: Mon - Sat, 11am - 5.30pm. Sun, 1.30 - 5.30pm, weekends in Oct: Sat, 11am - 5.30pm, Sun, 1.30 - 5.30pm. Last admission 4.30pm. Other times by appointment. Grounds: all year, daily, 9.30am - sunset.

Admission: Adult £4, Child £2.70, Family £10.70. Groups: Adult £3.20, Schools £1.

ℹ️ Shop. 🦽 Suitable. WCs. ☕ Tearoom. 🐄 In grounds, on leads.

CASTLE FRASER & GARDEN

J Dixon

SAUCHEN, INVERURIE AB51 7LD

Owner: *The National Trust for Scotland* ***Contact:*** *Eric Wilkinson*

Tel: 01330 833463

Over 400 years of history could be told if the stout walls of Castle Fraser could speak. Begun in 1575 by the 6th Laird, Michael Fraser, the two low wings contribute to the scale and magnificence of the towers rising above them, combining to make this the largest and most elaborate of the Scottish castles built on the 'Z' plan. The stunning simplicity of the Great Hall, which occupies the entire first floor of the main block, with its striking fireplace, almost 3 metres wide, immediately creates for the visitor the atmosphere of past centuries.

Location: OS Ref. NJ723 125. Off A944, 4m N of Dunecht & 16m W of Aberdeen.

Opening Times: Castle: Good Fri - Easter Mon, 1 May - 30 Jun and 1 - 30 Sept: daily, 1.30 - 5.30pm. 1 Jul - 30 Aug: daily, 11am - 5.30pm, weekends in Oct, 1.30 - 5.30pm, last admission 4.45pm. Tearoom; as castle but opens 12.15pm in Sept. Garden; all year, daily, 9.30am - 6pm. Grounds; all year, daily, 9.30 - sunset.

Admission: Adult £4, Child/Conc. £2.70. Groups: Adult £3.20. School £1. Family £10.70. Garden & grounds only: Adult £1.80, Child £1.20, Groups: Adult £1.50, Child/School £1.

ℹ️ Shop, plant sales. ☕ Tearoom.

CORGARFF CASTLE

Tel: 01975 651460

Strathdon

Owner: Historic Scotland   **Contact:** The Custodian

A 16th century tower house converted into a barracks for Hanoverian troops in 1748. Its last military use was to control the smuggling of illicit whisky between 1827 and 1831. Still complete and with star-shaped fortification.

Location: OS Ref. NJ255 086. 8m W of Strathdon on A939. 14m NW of Ballater.

Opening Times: 1 Apr - 30 Sept: Mon - Sat, 9.30am - 6.30pm, Sun, 2 - 6.30pm. 1 Oct - 31 Mar: Sat 9.30am - 4.30pm. Sun 2 - 4.30pm. Last admission ¹/₂ hr before closing.

Admission: Adult £2.30, Conc. £1.50, Child £1.

CRAIGIEVAR CASTLE

Tel: 013398 83635

Alford AB33 8JF

Owner: The National Trust for Scotland   **Contact:** David Mackay

Location: OS Ref. NJ566 095. On A980, 6m S of Alford and 26m W of Aberdeen.

Opening Times: Controlled access times during 1 May - 30 Sept. Please enquire.

Admission: Castle: Adult £5.20, Child £3.40, no groups. Family £13.80.

CRATHES CASTLE

BANCHORY AB31 3QJ

Owner: The National Trust for Scotland   *Contact:* William Bowman

Tel: 01330 844525

Fairytale-like turrets, gargoyles of fantastic design, superb painted ceilings and the ancient Horn of Leys given in 1323 to Alexander Burnett by King Robert the Bruce, are just a few of the exciting features at this most picturesque castle. The building of the castle began in 1553 and took 40 years to complete. Just over 300 years later, Sir James and Lady Burnett began developing the walled garden and created not just one but eight superb gardens which now provide a riot of colour throughout the summer.

Location: OS Ref. NO733 969. On A93, 3m E of Banchory and 15m W of Aberdeen.

Opening Times: Castle, visitor centre, shop & restaurant: Good Fri - 31 Oct: daily, 11am - 5.30pm, last admission to castle 4.45pm. Plant sales: same dates except weekends only in Oct. Other times by appointment only. Garden & grounds: all year, daily, 9.30am - sunset.

Admission: Adult £4.50, Child £3, Family £12. Group: Adult £3.60, School £1. Grounds only: Adult £1.80, Child £1.20, Family £4.80. Group: Adult £1.50, School £1.

i Shop, plant sales.   ☕ Restaurant.

CRUICKSHANK BOTANIC GARDEN

Tel: 01224 272704   **Fax:** 01224 272703

St Machar Drive, Aberdeen AB24 3UU

Owner: University of Aberdeen   **Contact:** R B Rutherford

Extensive collection of shrubs, herbaceous and alpine plants and trees. Rock and water gardens.

Location: OS Ref. NJ938 084. In old Aberdeen.

Opening Times: All year: Mon - Fri, 9am - 4.30pm. May - Sept: Sat and Sun only 2 - 5pm.

Admission: Free.

♿ Grounds suitable.   Ⓟ No parking.   🐄 In grounds, on leads.

DALLAS DHU DISTILLERY

Tel: 01309 676548

Forres

Owner: Historic Scotland   **Contact:** The Custodian

A completely preserved time capsule of the distiller's craft. Wander at will through this fine old Victorian distillery then enjoy a dram. Visitor centre, shop and audio-visual theatre.

Location: OS Ref. NJ035 566. 1m S of Forres off the A940.

Opening Times: 1 Apr - 30 Sept: Mon - Sat, 9.30am - 6.30pm, Sun, 2 - 6.30pm, last ticket 6pm. 1 Oct - 31 Mar: Mon - Sat, 9.30am - 4.30pm, Sun, 2 - 4.30pm, last ticket 4pm. Closed Thur pm and Fri in winter.

Admission: Adult £2.30, Conc. £1.50, Child £1.

DELGATIE CASTLE

TURRIFF, ABERDEENSHIRE AB53 8ED

Owner: Captain Hay of Delgatie   *Contact:* Mrs Joan Johnson

Tel: 01888 563479

11th century castle. Painted ceilings dated 1592 and 1597. Widest turnpike stair of its kind in Scotland. Lake and woodland walks.

Location: OS Ref. NJ754 506. Off A947 Aberdeen to Banff Road.

Opening Times: Apr - Oct: 10am - 5pm.

Admission: Adult £2.50, Child £1.20, OAP £1.50.

i Shop.   ♿ Ground floor suitable. WC.   ☕ Restaurant.
🏃 By arrangement.   🐕 Guide dogs only.   A Available.

Castle Fraser, Aberdeenshire.

DRUM CASTLE

DRUMOAK, BY BANCHORY AB31 3EY

Owner: The National Trust for Scotland   *Contact:* Mrs Krista Chisholm

Tel: 01330 811204

The combination over the years of a 13th century square tower, a very fine Jacobean mansion house and the additions of the Victorian lairds make Drum Castle unique among Scottish castles. Owned for 653 years by one family, the Irvines, every stone and every room is steeped in history. Superb furniture and paintings provide a visual feast for visitors. In the 16th century Chapel, the stained glass windows, the font copied from the Saxon one in Winchester Cathedral and the Augsburg silver Madonna, all add immense interest for visitors.

Location: OS Ref. NJ796 004. Off A93, 3m W of Peterculter and 10m W of Aberdeen.

Opening Times: Castle: Good Fri - Easter Mon, 1 May - 30 Sept; daily, 1.30 - 5.30pm. Weekends in Oct: 1.30 - 5.30pm, last admission 4.45pm. Garden; same dates, daily 10am - 6pm. Grounds; all year, daily, 9.30 - sunset.

Admission: Adult £4, Child £2.70, Family £10.70. Groups: Adult £3.20, School £1. Group visits must book. Gardens & grounds only: Adult £1.80, Child £1.20, Family £4.80. Groups: Adult £1.50, School £1.

FASQUE

FETTERCAIRN, KINCARDINESHIRE AB30 1DJ

Owner: Charles Gladstone   *Contact:* The Administrator

Tel: 01561 340202 or 340569 **Fax:** 01561 340325

A spectacular example of a Victorian 'upstairs - downstairs' stately home. Home to William Gladstone, four times Prime Minister, for much of his life. Inside very little has changed since Victorian times. See the famous double cantilever staircase, William Gladstone library, the extraordinary kitchen, and visit the family church. Deer park, picnic site and walks.

Location: OS Ref. NO648 755. On the B974, 1m N of Fettercairn, 4m from A90. Aberdeen/Dundee 35m.

Opening Times: 1 May - 30 Sept: daily 11am - 5.30pm. Groups by arrangement any time.

Admission: Adult £3.50, Conc. £2.50, Child £1.50.

ⓘ Shop.   ♿ Ground floor suitable.   ☕ Tearoom.
🚶 By arrangement.   🅿 Ample.   🐕 In grounds, on leads.

DUFF HOUSE

See page 19 for full page entry.

DUNNOTTAR CASTLE
Tel: 01569 762173

The Lodge, Stonehaven AB3 2TL

Contact: P McKenzie

Spectacular ruin. Impregnable fortress to the Earls Marischals of Scotland. The site for the successful protection of the Scottish Crown Jewels against the might of Cromwell's army. A castle dreams are made of. A must for anyone who takes Scottish history seriously.

Location: OS Ref. NO881 839. Just off A92. 1½ m SE of Stonehaven.

Opening Times: Easter - Oct: Mon - Sat, 9am - 6pm. Sun 2 - 5pm. Nov - Easter: Mon - Fri, 9am - sunset. Closed weekends. Last admission: 30 mins before closing.

Admission: Adult £3, Child £1.

♿ Not suitable.   ☕ Kiosk.   🅿 Ample.   🐕 In grounds, on leads.

ELGIN CATHEDRAL
Tel: 01343 547171

Elgin

Owner: Historic Scotland   **Contact:** The Custodian

When entire this was perhaps the most beautiful of Scottish cathedrals, known as the Lantern of the North. 13th century, much modified after almost being destroyed in 1390 by Alexander Stewart, the infamous 'Wolf of Badenoch'. The octagonal chapterhouse is the finest in Scotland. You can see the Bishop's home at Spynie Palace, 2m north of the town.

Location: OS Ref. NJ223 630. In Elgin on the A96.

Opening Times: 1 Apr - 30 Sept: Mon - Sat, 9.30am - 6.30pm, Sun, 2 - 6.30pm, last ticket 6pm. 1 Oct - 31 Mar: Mon - Sat, 9.30am - 4.30pm, Sun 2 - 4.30pm, last ticket 4pm. Closed Thur pm and Fri in winter.

Admission: Adult £1.20, Conc. 75p, Child 75p. Joint entry ticket with Spynie Palace: Adult £2.50, Conc. £1.50, Child £1.20.

FYVIE CASTLE

Glyn Satterley

TURRIFF, ABERDEENSHIRE AB53 8JS

Owner: The National Trust for Scotland   *Contact:* The Property Manager

Tel: 01651 891266

The south front of this magnificent building employs a plethora of crow-stepped gables, turrets, sculpted dormers and finials in the form of musicians, to create a marvellous façade. The five towers of the castle bear witness to the five families who have owned it. Fyvie Castle boasts the finest wheel stair in Scotland and there is a superb collection of arms and armour and paintings, including works by Batoni, Raeburn, Romney, Gainsborough, Opie and Hoppner.

Location: OS Ref. NJ763 393. Off A947, 8m SE of Turriff, and 25m N of Aberdeen.

Opening Times: Castle: Good Fri - 30 Jun, 1 - 30 Sept; daily 1.30 - 5.30pm. 1 Jul - 31 Aug; daily, 11am - 5.30pm. Weekends in Oct: 1.30 - 5.30pm, last admission 4.45pm. Tearoom, as castle but 12.30pm when castle opens at 1.30pm. Grounds: all year daily, 9.30am - sunset.

Admission: Adult £4, Child £2.70, Family £10.70. Groups: Adult £3.20, School £1.

ⓘ Shop.   ♿ Suitable, WC.   ☕ Tearoom.

HADDO HOUSE

TARVES, ELLON, ABERDEENSHIRE AB41 0ER

Owner: *The National Trust for Scotland*   **Contact:** *Craig Ferguson*

Tel: 01651 851440   **Fax:** 01651 851888

This appealing house was designed by William Adam in 1731 for William, 2nd Earl of Aberdeen. Much of the splendid interior is 'Adam Revival' carried out about 1880 for John, 7th Earl and 1st Marquess of Aberdeen and his Countess, Ishbel. It is arguably the most elegant house in the north east, a classic English-style stately home transplanted to Scotland. Features of the house include the Italianate sweeping twin staircases at the front of the house, the atmospheric library and the subtlety of the great curving corridor.

Location: OS Ref. NJ868 348. Off B999, 4m N of Pitmedden, 7m NW of Ellon.

Opening Times: House: Good Fri - Easter Mon, 1 May - 30 Sept; daily, 1.30 - 5.30pm. Weekends in Oct: 1.30 - 5.30pm last admission 4.45pm. Shop & restaurant: Good Fri - 30 Sept; daily, 11am - 5.30pm. Weekends in Oct & Nov: 11am - 5.30pm. Shop closed 26 - 27 Oct. Garden & country park; all year, daily, 9.30am - sunset.

Admission: Adult £4, Child £2.70, Family £10.70. Groups: Adult £3.20, School £1.

☕ Restaurant.

LEITH HALL

Jim Henderson

HUNTLY, ABERDEENSHIRE AB54 4NQ

Owner: *The National Trust for Scotland*   **Contact:** *Eileen Law*

Tel: 01464 831216

This mansion house is built around a courtyard and was the home of the Leith family for almost 400 years. With an enviable family record of military service over the centuries, the house contains a unique collection of military memorabilia displayed in an exhibition *'For Crown and Country'.* The graciously furnished rooms are a delight to wander through and present a fine impression of the lifestyle of the Leith family.

Location: OS Ref. NJ541 298. B9002, 1m W of Kennethmont, 7m S of Huntley.

Opening Times: House & tearoom: Good Fri - Easter Mon, 1 May - 30 Sept; daily, 1.30 - 5.30pm. Weekends in Oct: 1.30 - 5.30pm, last admission 4.45pm. Gardens & grounds; all year, daily, 9.30am - sunset.

Admission: Adult £4, Child £2.70, Family £10.70. Groups: Adult £3.20, School £1. Gardens & grounds: Adult £1.80, Child £1.20, Family £4.80. Groups: Adult £1.50, School £1.

☕ Tearoom.

HUNTLY CASTLE   **Tel:** 01466 793191

Huntly

Owner: Historic Scotland   **Contact:** The Custodian

Known also as Strathbogie Castle, this glorious ruin stands in a beautiful setting on the banks of the River Deveron. Famed for its fine heraldic sculpture and inscribed stone friezes.

Location: OS Ref. NJ532 407. In Huntly on the A96. N side of the town.

Opening Times: 1 Apr - 30 Sept: Mon - Sat, 9.30am - 6.30pm, Sun, 2 - 6.30pm, last ticket 6pm. 1 Oct - 31 Mar: Mon - Sat, 9.30am - 4.30pm, Sun 2 - 4.30pm, last ticket 4pm. Closed Thur pm and Fri in winter.

Admission: Adult £2.30, Conc £1.50, Child £1.

KILDRUMMY CASTLE   **Tel:** 01975 571331

Alford, Aberdeenshire

Owner: Historic Scotland   **Contact:** The Custodian

Though ruined, the best example in Scotland of a 13th century castle with a curtain wall, four round towers, hall and chapel of that date. The seat of the Earls of Mar, it was dismantled after the first Jacobite rising in 1715.

Location: OS Ref. NJ455 164. 10m W of Alford on the A97. 16m SSW of Huntley.

Opening Times: 1 Apr - 30 Sept: Mon - Sat, 9.30am - 6.30pm, Sun, 2 - 6.30pm, last ticket 6pm.

Admission: Adult £1.50, Conc. £1, Child 75p.

KILDRUMMY CASTLE GARDEN   **Tel:** 01975 571203 / 571277

Kildrummy, Aberdeenshire   **Contact:** Alastair J Laing

Ancient quarry, shrub and alpine gardens renowned for their interest and variety. Water gardens below ruined castle.

Location: OS Ref. NJ455 164. On A97 off A944 10m SW of Alford. 16m SSW of Huntley.

Opening Times: Apr - Oct: daily, 10am - 5pm.

Admission: Adult £1.70, Child 50p.

MONYMUSK WALLED GARDEN   **Tel:** 01467 651543

Home Farm, Monymusk, Aberdeen AB51 7H.

Owner: Mrs M Coleman   **Contact:** Mrs M Coleman

Mainly herbaceous plants in walled garden setting.

Opening Times: Nov - Mar: Mon, Wed, Fri & Sat, 10am - 3pm, Sun 12 noon - 3pm. Apr - Oct: Mon - Sat, 10am - 5pm, Sun 12 noon - 5pm.

Admission: Donations welcome.

PITMEDDEN GARDEN

Doug Westland

ELLON, ABERDEENSHIRE AB41 0PD

Owner: *The National Trust for Scotland*   **Contact:** *Douglas Westland*

Tel: 01651 842352

The centrepiece of this property is the Great Garden which was originally laid out in 1675 by Sir Alexander Seton, 1st Baronet of Pitmedden. The elaborate designs, inspired by the garden at the Palace of Holyroodhouse in Edinburgh, have been painstakingly recreated for the enjoyment of visitors. The 100-acre estate, contains the very fine Museum of Farming Life, which presents a vivid picture of the lives and times of bygone days when the horse was the power in front of the plough and farm machinery was less complicated than it is today.

Location: OS Ref. NJ885 280. On A920 1m W of Pitmedden village and 14m N of Aberdeen.

Opening Times: Garden, visitor centre, museum, grounds and other facilities: 1 May - 30 Sept; daily, 10am - 5.30pm, last admission 5pm.

Admission: Adult £3.50, Child £2.30, Family £9.30. Groups: Adult £2.80, School £1.

♿ Suitable.

ST MACHAR'S CATHEDRAL TRANSEPTS

Tel: 0131 668 8800

Old Aberdeen

Owner: Historic Scotland

The nave and towers of the Cathedral remain in use as a church, and the ruined transepts are in care. In the south transept is the fine altar tomb of Bishop Dunbar (1514 - 32).

Location: OS Ref. NJ939 088. In old Aberdeen. ¹/₂ m N of King's College.

Admission: Free.

SPYNIE PALACE

Tel: 01343 546358

Elgin

Owner: Historic Scotland   **Contact:** The Custodian

Spynie Palace was the residence of the Bishops of Moray from the 14th century to 1686. The site is dominated by the massive tower built by Bishop David Stewart (1461-77) and affords spectacular views across Spynie Loch.

Location: OS Ref. NJ231 659. 2m N of Elgin off the A941.

Opening Times: 1 Apr - 30 Sept: Mon - Sat, 9.30am - 6.30pm, Sun, 2 - 6.30pm. 1 Oct - 31 Mar: Sat, 9.30am - 4.30pm, Sun, 2 - 4.30pm. Last ticket 30mins before closing.

Admission: Adult £1.50, Conc. £1, Child 75p. Joint entry ticket with Elgin Cathedral: Adult £2.50, Conc. £1.50, Child £1.20.

TOLQUHON CASTLE

Tel: 01651 851286

Aberdeenshire

Owner: Historic Scotland   **Contact:** The Custodian

Tolquhon was built for the Forbes family. The early 15th century tower was enlarged between 1584 and 1589 with a large mansion around the courtyard. Noted for its highly ornamented gatehouse and pleasance.

Location: OS Ref. NJ874 286. 15m N of Aberdeen on the A920. 6m N of Ellon.

Opening Times: 1 Apr - 30 Sept: Mon - Sat, 9.30am - 6.30pm, Sun, 2 - 6.30pm. 1 Oct - 31 Mar: Sat, 9.30am - 4.30pm, Sun, 2 - 4.30pm. Last ticket ¹/₂ hr before closing.

Admission: Adult £1.50, Conc. £1, Child 75p.

Leith Hall, Aberdeenshire.

BOTHWELL CASTLE

Tel: 01698 816894

Uddingston, Strathclyde

Owner: Historic Scotland   **Contact:** The Custodian

The largest and finest 13th century stone castle in Scotland, much fought over during the Wars of Independence. Part of the original circular keep survives, but most of the castle dates from the 14th and 15th centuries. In a beautiful setting overlooking the Clyde.

Location: OS Ref. NS688 593. 1m NW of Bothwell. At Uddingston off the B7071.

Opening Times: 1 Apr - 30 Sept: Mon - Sat, 9.30am - 6.30pm, Sun, 2 - 6.30pm, last ticket 6pm. 1 Oct - 31 Mar: Mon - Sat, 9.30am - 4.30pm, Sun, 2 - 4.30pm, last ticket 4pm. Closed Thur pm and Fri in winter.

Admission: Adult £1.50, Conc £1, Child 75p.

CHATELHERAULT HUNTING LODGE   **Tel:** 01698 426213   **Fax:** 01698 4215327

Ferniegair, by Hamilton ML3 7UE

Owner: South Lanarkshire Council   **Contact:** Morvern Anderson

Built for James, 5th Duke of Hamilton, designed by William Adam, completed around 1744. Set in 500 acre country park.

Location: OS Ref. NS737 540. W side of A72, 1½ m SE of Hamilton.

Opening Times: All year except Christmas and New Year.

i Shop.   Ground floor & grounds suitable.   Tearoom.   Guide dogs only.

COLZIUM HOUSE & WALLED GARDEN

Tel/Fax: 01236 823281

Colzium - Lennox Estate, off Stirling Road, Kilsyth G65 0RZ

Owner: Cumbernauld & Kilsyth District Council   **Contact:** A C Spiers

A walled garden with an extensive collection of conifers, rare shrubs and trees. Kilsyth Heritage Museum, curling pond, tearoom, picnic tables, pitch and putt, woodland walks.

Location: OS Ref. NS762 786. Off A803 Banknock to Kirkintilloch Road. ½ m E of Kilsyth.

Opening Times: Walled garden: 12 - 7pm. Easter - Sept: Museum in house: 2 -5pm, Wed. Apr - Sept or by appointment.

Admission: Free. Charge for pitch and putt.

Tearoom.

CRAIGNETHAN CASTLE

Tel: 01555 86364

Lanark, Strathclyde

Owner: Historic Scotland   **Contact:** The Custodian

In a picturesque setting overlooking the River Nethan and defended by a wide and deep ditch with an unusual caponier, a stone vaulted artillery chamber, unique in Britain.

Location: OS Ref. NS815 463. 5½ m WNW of Lanark off the A72. ½ m footpath to W.

Opening Times: 1 Mar - 31 Oct: closed Thur pm and Fri in Mar & Oct.

Admission: Adult £1.50, Conc. £1, Child 75p.

FINLAYSTONE

LANGBANK, RENFREWSHIRE PA14 6TJ

Owner: *Mr George MacMillan*   **Contact:** *Mr George MacMillan*

Tel: 01475 540285   **Fax:** 01475 540713

Overlooking the River Clyde, Finlaystone was the home of the Earls of Glencairn for 4 centuries and is now the home of the Chief of the Clan MacMillan. Visitors to this delightful country estate can explore beautiful gardens and woodlands, and have the opportunity to view a unique doll collection in the visitor centre which also houses natural history, Celtic art and Clan MacMillan displays and information. Fun for all the family with children's play areas and ranger service.

Location: OS Ref. NS390 730. On A8, 7m W of Glasgow airport.

Opening Times: House: Apr - Aug: Sun, guided tours at 2pm, 3pm & 4pm. Grounds; all year, 10.30am - 5pm. Refreshments & visitor centre: Apr - Sept: daily, 11am - 4.30pm.

Admission: Grounds: Adult £2, Child/Conc. £1.20. Extra for House: Adult £1.50, Child/Conc. £1.30. Dolly Mixture: 50p.

i Shop.   Ground floor & grounds suitable. WC.   Tearoom.
P Ample.   In grounds, on leads.

Torosay Castle, Isle of Mull (West Highlands).

GLASGOW CATHEDRAL

Tel: 0141 552 6891

Glasgow

Owner: Historic Scotland   **Contact:** The Custodian

The only Scottish mainland medieval cathedral to have survived the Reformation complete. Built over the tomb of St Kentigern. Notable features in this splendid building are the elaborately vaulted crypt, the stone screen of the early 15th century and the unfinished Blackadder Aisle.

Location: OS Ref. NS603 656. E end of city centre. In central Glasgow.

GREENBANK

John K Wilkie

CLARKSTON, GLASGOW G76 8RB

Owner: The National Trust for Scotland   *Contact:* Mr Jim May

Tel: 0141 639 3281

Be allured by the beautiful bronze water nymph 'Foam' whose exquisite form complements the circular pool and surrounding greenery. There are several small gardens including a parterre layout illustrating different aspects of gardening. The larger borders contain a wide range of shrub roses and perennial and annual flowers.

Location: OS Ref. NS563 566. Flenders Road, off Mearns Road, Clarkston. Off M77 and A726, 6m S of Glasgow city centre.

Opening Times: All year, daily, 9.30am - sunset, except 25 & 26 Dec and 1 & 2 Jan. Shop & tearoom: Good Fri - 31 Oct, daily, 11am - 5pm. 1 Nov - 31 Mar: Sat & Sun, 2 - 4pm. House: 1 Apr - 31 Oct: Sun only and during special events (subject to functions in progress).

Admission: Adult £2.80, Child £1.90, Family £7.50. Groups: Adult £2.30, School £1.

ℹ Shop.   ♿ Grounds suitable. WC.   ☕ Tearoom.   🐕 In grounds, on leads.

HUTCHESONS' HALL

Tel: 0141 552 8391   **Fax:** 0141 552 7031

158 Ingram Street, Glasgow G1 1EJ

Owner: The National Trust for Scotland   **Contact:** Jeanette Macaulay

Described as one of Glasgow city centre's most elegant buildings, the Hall by David Hamilton, replaced the earlier 1641 hospice founded by George and Thomas Hutcheson. Reconstructed in 1876, the building is now 'A-Listed' as being of national importance.

Location: OS Ref NS594 652. Glasgow city centre, near SE corner of George Square.

Opening Times: Visitor centre/shop/function hall: all year (except BHs & 24 Dec - 6 Jan), Mon - Sat, 10am - 5pm. (Hall on view subject to functions in progress). Shop closed for stocktaking 1/2 Nov.

Admission: Free.

ℹ Shop. Conferences.   ✗ Available for up to 120.   ♿ WCs.   🚶 By arrangement.

NEWARK CASTLE

Tel: 01475 741858

Port Glasgow, Strathclyde

Owner: Historic Scotland   **Contact:** The Custodian

The oldest part of the castle is a tower built soon after 1478 with a detached gatehouse, by George Maxwell. The main part was added in 1597 - 99 in a most elegant style. Enlarged in the 16th century by his descendent, the wicked Patrick Maxwell who murdered two of his neighbours.

Location: OS Ref. NS329 744. In Port Glasgow on the A8.

Opening Times: 1 Apr - 30 Sept: Mon - Sat, 9.30am - 6.30pm, Sun, 2 - 6.30pm, last ticket 6pm.

Admission: Adult £1.50, Conc. £1, Child 75p.

POLLOK HOUSE

Tel: 0141 632 0274   **Fax:** 0141 649 0823

Glasgow G43 1AT

Owner: City of Glasgow District Council   **Contact:** The Administrator

Early 18th century house, containing the remarkable Stirling Maxwell collection of Spanish paintings. Nearby in Pollok Park is the Burrell Collection.

Location: OS Ref. NS550 616. 2m SW of Glasgow city centre via M77 & A736.

Opening Times: Mon - Sat, 10am - 5pm. Sun 11am - 5pm. (unconfirmed for 1997).

Admission: Free.

ST ANDREW'S CATHEDRAL

Tel: 0141 339 669

Glasgow G1 4ER   **Contact:** Sally-Anne Porter

The earliest Catholic church (post reformation) in the Glasgow area. Built in 1816.

Location: OS Ref. NS590 647. Clyde Street, central Glasgow on N Bank of Clyde.

Opening Times: All year: 8am - 6pm. Sun services: 10am, 12 & 5pm. Weekday services: 8.15am, 1pm and 5.15pm.

ST MARY'S CATHEDRAL

Tel/Fax: 0141 339 6691

300 Great Western Road, Glasgow G4 9JB   **Contact:** Sally Anne Porter

Fine Gothic Revival church by Sir George Gilbert Scott, with outstanding contemporary murals by Gwyneth Leech.

Location: OS Ref. NS578 669. ¼ m after the Dumbarton A82 exit from M8 motorway.

Opening Times: Mon - Fri, 9.30am - 5.45pm, Sat, 9.30am - 12 noon. Sun services: 8.30am, 10am, 12 noon and 6.30pm. Weekday services: please telephone.

THE TENEMENT HOUSE

145 BUCCLEUCH STREET, GLASGOW G3 6QN

Owner: The National Trust for Scotland   *Contact:* Miss Lorna Hepburn

Tel: 0141 333 0183

A typical Victorian tenement flat of 1892, and fascinating time capsule of the first half of the 20th century. It was the home of an ordinary Glasgow shorthand typist, who lived up this 'wally close' for more than 50 years. It is exceptional as the gaslit flat retains many of its original fittings and items such as her mother's sewing machine.

Location: OS Ref. NS583 662. Garnethill, (three streets N of Sauchiehall Street, near Charing Cross), Glasgow.

Opening Times: 1 Mar - 31 Oct; daily, 2 - 5pm, last admission 4.30pm. Weekday morning visits by educational and other groups (max 15) by booking only.

Admission: Adult £2.80, Child £1.90, Family £7.50. Groups: Adult £2.30, School £1.

♿ Not suitable.   🅿 Limited.

WEAVER'S COTTAGE

Tel: 01505 705588

Shuttle Street, Kilbarchan, Renfrew PA10 2JG

Owner: The National Trust for Scotland   **Contact:** Grace Murray

Typical cottage of an 18th century handloom weaver contains looms, weaving equipment and domestic utensils. Attractive cottage garden. Occasional weaving demonstrations.

Location: OS Ref. NS402 633. Off A740 (off M8) and A737, at The Cross, Kilbarchan, (nr Johnstone, Paisley) 12m SW of Glasgow.

Opening Times: Good Fri - 30 Sept; daily, 1.30 - 5.30pm. Weekends in Oct: 1.30 - 5.30pm. Last admission 5pm.

Admission: Adult £1.80, Child £1.20, Family £4.80. Groups: Adult £1.50, School £1.

CAWDOR CASTLE
Nairn

This splendid romantic castle dating from the late 14th century was built as a private fortress by the Thanes of Cawdor, and remains the home of the Cawdor family to this day. The ancient medieval tower was built around the legendary holly tree.

Although the house has evolved over 600 years, later additions mainly of the 17th century were all built in the Scottish vernacular style with slated roofs over walls and crow-stepped gables of mellow local stone. This style gives Cawdor a strong sense of unity, and the massive, severe exterior belies an intimate interior that gives the place a surprisingly personal, friendly atmosphere.

Good furniture, fine portraits and pictures, interesting objects and outstanding tapestries are arranged to please the family rather than to echo fashion or impress. Memories of Shakespeare's *Macbeth* give Cawdor an elusive, evocative quality that delights visitors.

GARDENS

The flower garden also has a family feel to it, where plants are chosen out of affection rather than affectation. This is a lovely spot between spring and late summer. The walled garden has been restored with a holly maze, paradise garden, knot garden and thistle garden. The wild garden beside its stream leads into beautiful trails through a spectacular mature mixed woodland, through which paths are helpfully marked and colour-coded.

CONTACT

The Secretary
Cawdor Castle
Nairn
Scotland
IV12 5RD

Tel: (01667) 404615

Fax: (01667) 404674

LOCATION

OS Ref. NH850 500

From Edinburgh
A9, 3$\frac{1}{2}$ hrs,
Inverness 20 mins,
Nairn 10 mins.
Main road: A9, 14m.

Rail: Nairn Station
5m.

Bus: Inverness to Nairn
bus route 200 yds.

Taxi: Nairn Taxis
(01667) 455342

Air: Inverness Airport 5m.

OPENING TIMES

SUMMER

1 May - 12 October
daily, 10am - 5.30pm.

Last admission 5pm.

WINTER

13 October - 30 April
Closed.

ADMISSION

SUMMER
House & Garden
Adult £5.00
Child* £2.70
OAP........................£4.00
Family (2+5) £13.50

Groups (Min 20)
Adult £4.50
Child* £2.70

Garden only
Adult £2.70
Child* £2.70
OAP........................£2.70

*Age 5 - 15

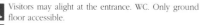

i Gift, book and wool shops. Conferences, 9 hole golf course, putting green, golf clubs for hire, whisky tasting, musical entertainments, specialised garden visits. No photography, video taping or tripods inside.

X Lunches, sherry or champagne receptions.

Visitors may alight at the entrance. WC. Only ground floor accessible.

Licensed buttery, May-Oct, groups should book.

P 250 cars and 25 coaches. Two weeks' notice for group catering, coach drivers/couriers free.

Welcome, £2.20 per child. Room notes, quiz and answer sheet can be provided. Ranger service and nature trails.

No dogs.

CONFERENCE/FUNCTION		
ROOM	SIZE	MAX CAPACITY
Cawdor Hall		40

DUNVEGAN CASTLE
Isle of Skye

DUNVEGAN is unique. It is the only Great House in the Western Isles of Scotland to have retained its family and its roof. It is the oldest home in the whole of Scotland continuously inhabited by the same family - the Chiefs of the Clan Macleod. A Castle placed on a rock by the sea - the curtain wall is dated before 1200 A.D. - its superb location recalls the Norse Empire of the Vikings, the ancestors of the Chiefs.

Dunvegan's continuing importance as a custodian of the Clan spirit is epitomised by the famous Fairy Flag, whose origins are shrouded in mystery but whose ability to protect both Chief and Clan is unquestioned. To enter Dunvegan is to arrive at a place whose history combines with legend to make a living reality.

GARDENS
The gardens and grounds extend over some ten acres of woodland walks, peaceful formal lawns and a water garden dominated by two spectacular natural waterfalls. The temperate climate aids in producing a fine show of rhododendrons and azaleas, the chief glory of the garden in spring. Always one is aware of the proximity of the sea and many garden walks finish at the Castle Jetty, from where traditional boats make regular trips to view the delightful Seal Colony.

CONTACT

The Administrator
Dunvegan Castle
Isle of Skye
Scotland
IV55 8WF

Tel: (01470) 521206

Fax: (01470) 521205

LOCATION

OS Ref. NG250 480

1m N of village. NW corner of Skye.

From Inverness A82 to Invermoriston, A887 to Kyle of Lochalsh 82m. From Fort William A82 to Invergarry, A87 to Kyle of Lochalsh 76m.

Kyle of Lochalsh to Dunvegan 45m via Skye Bridge (toll).

Ferry: To the Isle of Skye, 'roll-on, roll-off', 30 minute crossing.

Rail: Inverness to Kyle of Lochalsh 3 - 4 trains per day - 45m.

Bus: Portree 25m, Kyle of Lochalsh 45m.

i Gift and craft shop. Boat trips to seal colony. Loch cruises, charter and fishing trips, pedigree Highland cattle. No photography in castle.

Visitors may alight at entrance. WC.

Licensed restaurant (cap 70) special rates for groups, menus upon request. Tel: (01470) 521310. Open late peak season for evening meals.

By appointment in English or Gaelic at no extra charge. If requested owner may meet groups, tour time 45mins.

P 120 cars and 10 coaches. Do not attempt to take passengers to Castle Jetty (long walk). If possible please book. Seal boat trip dependent upon weather.

Welcome by arrangement. Guide available on request.

In grounds only, on lead.

A 4 self-catering units, 3 of which sleep 6 and 1 of which sleeps 7.

OPENING TIMES

SUMMER

17 March - 31 October
daily: 10am - 5.30pm.
Last admission 5pm.

WINTER

11am - 4pm.

ADMISSION

SUMMER

Castle
Adult £4.80
Child (under 16) £2.60
OAP/Student...........£4.20
Group £4.20

Garden
Adult £3.50
Child (under 16) £1.80

Seal Boats
Adult £3.70
Child (under 16) £2.50

Loch Cruises
Adult £7.00
Child/Conc. £5.00

WINTER

11am - 4pm.
No boat trips.

ATTADALE GARDENS

By STRATHCARRON, ROSS-SHIRE IV54 8YX

Owner: Mr & Mrs Ewen Macpherson　　*Contact: Mr & Mrs Ewen Macpherson*

Tel: 01520 722217

The garden and woodland walks were planted by the Schroder family from 1890 onwards with species rhododendrons, azaleas and southern hemisphere plants made possible by the warm gulf stream. Spectacular water gardens with primula, iris and giant gunnera. Hill and cliff walks with views of Skye and the sea. Victorian sunken garden by the house. Waterproof shoes recommended.

Location: OS Ref. NG920 400. On A890 between Strathcarron and South Strome. 12m N of A87.

Opening Times: 1 Apr - 31 Oct: Mon - Sat, 10am - 5.30pm. Closed 1 - 2pm.

Admission: Adult £2, Child £1. Coaches/guided tours by prior arrangement.

WC.　　**P** Ample.　　In grounds, on leads.

CASTLE STALKER

Tel: 01883 622768　**Fax:** 01883 626238

Portnacroish, Appin, Argyll

Owner: Mrs M Allward　　　　　　**Contact:** Messrs R & A Allward

Early 15th century Tower House and ancient seat of the Stewarts of Appin. Picturesquely set on a rocky islet approx 400 yds off the mainland on the shore of Loch Linnhe. Reputed to have been used by James IV as a hunting lodge. Garrisoned by Government troops during the 1745 rising. Restored from a ruin by the late Lt Col Stewart Allward following acquisition in 1965 and now retained by his family.

Location: OS Ref. NM930 480. Approx. 20m N of Oban on the A828. On islet ¼ m offshore.

Opening Times: Apr - Sept for 25 days. Telephone for details. Times variable depending on tides and weather.

Admission: Adult £6, Child £3.

i Not suitable for coach parties.　　Not suitable.

CAWDOR CASTLE

See page 27 for full page entry.

CLAN DONALD VISITOR CENTRE & ARMADALE GARDEN

Armadale, Isle of Skye IV45 8RS　　**Tel:** 01471 844305　**Fax:** 01471 844275

Owner: Clan Donald Lands Trust　　　**Contact:** R McDonald Parker

Part of Armadale Castle houses a visitor centre telling the story of the Macdonalds and the Lord of the Isles. 40 acres of 19th century woodland garden.

Location: OS Ref. NG630 020. 1m N of the Mallaig - Armadale ferry terminal.

Opening Times: Apr - Oct: daily 9.30am - 5.30pm.

Admission: Adult £3.40, Child £2.20, Conc./Groups £2.20.

i Shop.　　Grounds suitable. WC.　　Licensed restaurant.　　In grounds, on leads.

CROMARTY COURTHOUSE

Tel: 01381 600418　**Fax:** 01381 600408

Church Street, Cromarty IV11 8XA

Contact: David Alston

18th century village courthouse, visitor centre and museum.

Location: OS Ref. NH790 680. 25m N of Inverness.

Opening Times: Please phone for details.

BALLINDALLOCH CASTLE

GRANTOWN-ON-SPEY, BANFFSHIRE AB37 9AX

Owner: Mr & Mrs Russell　　*Contact: Mrs Clare Russell*

Tel: 01807 500206　**Fax:** 01807 500210

Ballindalloch is a much loved family home and one of the few castles lived in continuously by its original owners, the Macpherson-Grants, since 1546. Filled with family memorabilia and a magnificent collection of 17th century Spanish paintings, it is home to the famous breed of Aberdeen Angus cattle. Beautiful rock and rose garden, river walks.

Location: OS Ref. NJ178 366. 14m NE of Grantown-on-Spey on A95, 22m S of Elgin on A95.

Opening Times: Good Fri - 30 Sept: 10am - 5pm.

Admission: Adult £3.95, Child (under 5) Free (6 - 16) £2, Disabled £1.50. Groups: (min 12) Adult £3.50. Garden only: £1.50.

i Shop.　　Ground floor & grounds. WC.　　Tearoom.

P Ample.　　Audio-Visual.　　In grounds, on leads.

CULLODEN

CULLODEN MOOR, INVERNESS IV1 2ED

Owner: The National Trust for Scotland　　*Contact: Ross Mackenzie*

Tel: 01463 790607　**Fax:** 01463 794294

No name in Scottish history evokes more emotion than that of Culloden, the bleak moor which in 1746 saw the hopes of the young Prince Charles Edward Stuart crushed, and the end of the Jacobite Rising, the 'Forty-Five'. The Prince's forces, greatly outnumbered by those of the brutal Duke of Cumberland, nevertheless went into battle with a courage which has passed into legend.

Location: OS Ref. NH745 450. On B9006, 5m E of Inverness.

Opening Times: Site; all year, daily. Visitor centre: 1 Feb - 31 Mar & 1 Nov - 30 Dec (except 25/26 Dec); daily, 10am - 4pm. 1 Apr - 31 Oct; daily, 9am - 6pm. Restaurant & audio visual; same dates but closes 30 mins earlier.

Admission: Adult £2.80, Child £1.90, Family £7.50. Groups: Adult £2.30, School £1.

i Shop (closed 1 - 7 Nov) & visitor centre.　　Suitable. WC.　　Restaurant.

Audio visual show.　　In dog walking area only.

DOCHFOUR GARDENS

Tel: 01463 861218

Dochgarroch, Inverness IV3 6JY

Owner: The Lord Burton   **Contact:** Lady Burton

Victorian terraced garden near Inverness with panoramic views over Loch Dochfour. Magnificent specimen trees, naturalised daffodils, rhododendrons, water garden, yew topiary.

Location: OS Ref. NH620 610. 6m SW of Inverness on A82 to Fort William.

Opening Times: Gardens: All year: Mon - Fri. Summer: Sat & Sun, 10am - 5pm. House not open.

Admission: Garden walk - £1.50.

i Plant sales.

DUNROBIN CASTLE

GOLSPIE, SUTHERLAND KW10 6SF

Owner: *The Sutherland Trust*   **Contact:** *Keith Jones, Curator*

Tel: 01408 633268 **Fax:** 01408 634081

Dates from the 13th century with additions in the 17th, 18th and 19th centuries. Wonderful furniture, paintings, library, ceremonial robes and memorabilia. Victorian museum in grounds with a fascinating collection including Pictish stones. Set in fine woodlands overlooking the sea. Magnificent formal gardens, one of few remaining French/Scottish formal parterres.

Location: OS Ref. NC850 010. 50m N of Inverness on A9. 1m NE of Golspie.

Opening Times: 28 Mar - 31 May & 1 - 15 Oct: Mon - Sat, 10.30am - 4.30pm. Sun, 12 - 4.30pm. 1 Jun - 30 Sept: Mon - Sat, 10.30am - 5.30pm. Sun, 12 - 5.30pm.

Admission: Adult £4.80, Child £2.40, Conc. £3.20. Groups: Adult £4.40, Child £2.20, Conc £2.80. Family (2+2) £12.

i Gift shop.   ☕ Restaurant.

DUNVEGAN CASTLE

See page 28 for full page entry.

EILEAN DONAN CASTLE

Tel: 01599 555202

Dornie, Kyle, Wester IV40 8DX

Contact: The Administrator

Picturesque castle on an islet dating back to 1220.

Location: OS Ref. NG880 260. On A87 8m E of Skye Ferry.

Opening Times: Easter - end Oct: 10am - 5.30pm.

Admission: Adult £3, Conc./Groups £1.50.

i Shop.   ♿ Not suitable.   P Ample.   🐕 In grounds, on leads.

FORT GEORGE

Tel: 01667 462777

Ardersier, Inverness-shire

Owner: Historic Scotland   **Contact:** The Custodian

Completed in 1769, following the Battle of Culloden, as a Highland fortress for the army of George II. Fort George is still an active army barracks which houses the Regimental Museum of the Queen's Own Highlanders.

Location: OS Ref. NH762 567. 10m W of Nairn, 11m NE of Inverness off the A96.

Opening Times: 1 Apr - 30 Sept: Mon - Sat, 9.30am - 6.30pm, Sun, 2 - 6.30pm, last ticket 5.45pm. 1 Oct - 31 Mar: Mon - Sat, 9.30am - 4.30pm, Sun, 2 - 4.30pm, last ticket 3.45pm.

Admission: Adult £2.80, Conc. £1.80, Child £1.

GLENFINNAN

INVERNESS-SHIRE PH37 4LT

Owner: *The National Trust for Scotland*   **Contact:** *Mrs Lillias Grant*

Tel/Fax: 01397 722250

The monument, situated on the scenic road to the Isles, is set amid superb Highland scenery at the head of Loch Shiel. It was erected in 1815 in tribute to the clansmen who fought and died in the Jacobite cause. Prince Charles Edward Stuart's standard was raised near here in 1745. Despite its inspired beginnings, the campaign came to a grim conclusion on the Culloden battlefield in 1746.

Location: OS Ref. NM906 805. On A830, 18m W of Fort William, Lochaber.

Opening Times: Site; all year, daily. Visitor centre & snack bar: 28 Mar - 18 May and 1 Sept - 31 Oct; daily, 10am - 1pm & 2 - 5pm. 19 May - 31 Aug; daily, 9.30am - 6pm (snack bar 10am - 6pm).

Admission: Adult £1, Child 60p, Family £2.60.

i Shop. Visitor centre.   ♿ Grounds suitable. WC.   ☕ Snack bar.
P Ample.   🐑 In grounds, on leads.

HUGH MILLER'S COTTAGE

CROMARTY IV11 8XA

Owner: *The National Trust for Scotland*   **Contact:** *Ms Frieda Gostwick*

Tel: 01381 600245

Furnished thatch cottage of c.1698, birthplace of eminent geologist and writer Hugh Miller. Exhibition and video.

Location: OS Ref. NH790 680. Via Kessock Bridge & A832, in Cromarty, 22m NE of Inverness.

Opening Times: 1 May - 30 Sept: Mon - Sat, 10am - 1pm & 2 - 5.30pm. Sun 2 - 5.30pm.

Admission: Adult £1.80, Child £1.20, Family £4.80. Groups: Adult £1.50, School £1.

♿ Not suitable.   P No parking.   🦮 Guide dogs only.

INVEREWE GARDEN

Brian Chapple

POOLEWE, ROSS & CROMARTY IV22 2LQ

Owner: *The National Trust for Scotland*   ***Contact:*** *Keith Gordon*

Tel: 01445 781200   **Fax:** 01445 781497

Where in Scotland will you see the tallest Australian gum trees in Britain, sweetly scented Chinese rhododendrons, exotic trees from Chile and Blue Nile lilies from South Africa, all growing on a latitude more northerly than Moscow? The answer is Inverewe. Miraculous? Yes and no, although you are in a remote corner of Wester Ross, you are also in a sheltered garden, blessed by the North Atlantic Drift. In a spectacular lochside setting among pinewoods, Osgood Mackenzie's Victorian dreams have produced a glorious 50 acre mecca for garden lovers.

Location: OS Ref. NG860 820. On A832, by Poolewe, 6m NE of Gairloch, Highland.

Opening Times: Garden: 15 Mar - 31 Oct; daily, 9.30am - 9pm. 1 Nov - 14 Mar; daily, 9.30 - 5pm. Visitor centre & shop: 15 Mar - 30 Sept; daily, 9.30am - 5.30pm. Restaurant; same dates, daily, 10am - 5pm. Guided walks: 15 Mar - 30 Oct: Mon - Fri at 1.30pm.

Admission: Adult £4.50, Child £3, Family £12. Groups: Adult £3.60, School £1.

ℹ️ Shop & visitor centre.   ♿ Grounds suitable. WC.   ☕ Licensed restaurant.
🅿️ Ample (no shaded parking for dogs).   🐕 Guide dogs only.

ROTHIEMURCHUS

THE DOUNE OF ROTHIEMURCHUS, BY AVIEMORE PH22 1QH

Owner: *J P Grant of Rothiemurchus*   ***Contact:*** *Rothiemurchus Visitor Centre*

Tel: 01479 810858   **Fax:** 01479 811778

The family home of The Grants of Rothiemurchus was nearly lost as a ruin and has been under an ambitious repair programme since 1975. This exciting project may be visited on selected Mondays throughout the year. Book with the visitor centre for a longer 2 hr 'Highland Lady' tour which explores the haunts of Elizabeth Grant of Rothiemurchus, born 1797, author of *Memoirs of a Highland Lady*, who vividly described the Doune and its surroundings from the memories of her childhood. Pheasant shoots, multi-activity days, receptions.

Location: OS Ref. NH900 100. 2m S of Aviemore on E bank of Spey river.

Opening Times: Grounds: May - Aug: Mon, 10am - 12.30pm and 2 - 4.30pm. Also first Mon of the month in winter.

Admission: Doune Grounds: £1pp. Guided Highland Lady Tour: £5pp, min charge of £20. Booking essential.

ℹ️ Shop. Visitor centre.   🚶 Compulsory.   🅿️ Limited.   🐕 In grounds, on leads.

URQUHART CASTLE 🏰

Tel: 01456 450551

Drumnadrochit, Loch Ness

Owner: Historic Scotland   **Contact:** The Custodian

The remains of one of the largest castles in Scotland dominate a rocky promontory on Loch Ness. It fell into decay after 1689. Most of the existing buildings date from the 16th century. A popular viewpoint for monster spotting. Splendid views up and down the loch.

Location: OS Ref. NH531 286. On Loch Ness, 1 1/2 m S of Drumnadrochit on A82.

Opening Times: 1 Apr - 30 Sept: Mon - Sun, 9.30am - 6.30pm, last ticket 5.45pm. 1 Oct - 31 Mar: Mon - Sun, 9.30am - 4.30pm, last ticket 3.45pm.

Admission: Adult £3.20, Conc. £2.20, Child £1.

Ballindalloch Castle, Banffshire.

BISHOP'S & EARL'S PALACES

Tel: 01856 875461

Kirkwall, Orkney

Owner: Historic Scotland   **Contact:** The Custodian

The Bishop's Palace is a 12th century hall-house with a round tower built by Bishop Reid in 1541-48. The adjacent Earl's Palace built in 1607 has been described as the most mature and accomplished piece of Renaissance architecture left in Scotland.

Location: Bishop's Palace: OS Ref. HY447 108. Earl's Palace: OS Ref. HY448 108. In Kirkwall on A960.

Opening Times: 1 Apr - 30 Sept: Mon - Sat, 9.30am - 6.30pm, Sun, 2 - 6.30pm, last ticket 6pm.

Admission: Adult £1.50, Conc. £1, Child 75p. Joint entry ticket available for all the Orkney monuments: Adult £7, Conc. £4.50, Child £2.50.

BLACK HOUSE

Tel: 01851 710395

Arnol, Isle of Lewis

Owner: Historic Scotland   **Contact:** The Custodian

A traditional Lewis thatched house, fully furnished, complete with attached barn, byre and stockyard. A peat fire burns in the open hearth.

Location: OS Ref. NB320 500. In Arnol village, 11m NW of Stornoway on A858.

Opening Times: 1 Apr - 30 Sept: Mon - Sat, 9.30am - 6.30pm, Sun, 2 - 6.30pm, last ticket 6pm. 1 Oct - 31 Mar: Mon - Sat, 9.30am - 4.30pm, last ticket 4pm. Closed Fri in winter.

Admission: Adult £1.50, Conc. £1, Child 75p.

BROCH OF GURNESS

Tel: 01831 579478

Aikerness, Orkney

Owner: Historic Scotland   **Contact:** The Custodian

Protected by three lines of ditch and rampart, the base of the broch is surrounded by a warren of Iron Age buildings.

Location: OS Ref. HY383 268. At Aikerness, about 14m NW of Kirkwall on A966.

Opening Times: 1 Apr - 30 Sept: Mon - Sat, 9.30am - 6.30pm, Sun, 2 - 6.30pm, last ticket 6pm.

Admission: Adult £2.30, Child £1, Conc. £1.50. Joint entry ticket available for all Orkney monuments: Adult £7, Conc. £4.50, Child £2.50.

JARLSHOF PREHISTORIC & NORSE SETTLEMENT

Tel: 01950 460112

Shetland

Owner: Historic Scotland   **Contact:** The Custodian

Over 3 acres of remains spanning 3,000 years from the Stone Age. Oval shaped Bronze Age houses, Iron Age broch and wheel houses. Viking long houses, medieval farmstead and 16th century laird's house.

Location: OS Ref. HY401 096. At Sumburgh Head, 22m S of Lerwick on the A970.

Opening Times: 1 Apr - 30 Sept: Mon - Sat 9.30am - 6.30pm, Sun 2 - 6.30pm. Last admission 1/2 hr before closing.

Admission: Adult £2.30, Conc. £1.50, Child £1.

MAES HOWE

Tel: 01856 761606

Orkney

Owner: Historic Scotland   **Contact:** The Custodian

This world famous tomb was built in Neolithic times, before 2700 BC. The large mound covers a stone-built passage and a burial chamber with cells in the walls. Runic inscriptions tell of how it was plundered of its treasures by Vikings.

Location: OS Ref. NY318 128. 9m W of Kirkwall on the A965.

Opening Times: 1 Apr - 30 Sept: Mon - Sat 9.30am - 6.30pm, Sun 2 - 6.30pm. 1 Oct - 31 Mar: Mon - Wed & Sat, 9.30am - 4.30pm.

Admission: Adult £2.30, Conc. £1.50, Child £1. Joint entry ticket available for all Orkney monuments: Adult £7, Conc. £4.50, Child £2.50. Admission, shop and refreshments at nearby Tormiston Mill.

SKARA BRAE

Tel: 01856 841815

Orkney

Owner: Historic Scotland   **Contact:** The Custodian

Uncovered by a storm in 1850 Skara Brae is one of the best preserved groups of Stone Age houses in western Europe. The houses contain stone furniture, hearths and drains and present a remarkable picture of life in Neolithic times.

Location: OS Ref. HY231 188. 19m NW of Kirkwall on the B9056.

Opening Times: 1 Apr - 30 Sept: Mon - Sat, 9.30am - 6.30pm. Sun 2 - 6.30pm. 1 Oct - 31 Mar: Mon - Sat, 9.30am - 4.30pm. Sun 2 - 4.30pm. Last admission 1/2 hour before closing.

Admission: Adult £2.80, Conc. £1.80, Child £1. Joint entry ticket available for all Orkney monuments: Adult £7, Conc. £4.50, Child £2.50.

Torosay Castle, Isle of Mull – the statue walk (West Highlands).

Brodick Castle, Isle of Arran – the drawing room (South of Scotland).

Culzean Castle, Ayrshire – the picture room (South of Scotland)

BLAIR CASTLE
Pitlochry

BLAIR CASTLE has been the ancient home and fortress of the Earls and Dukes of Atholl for over 725 years. Its central location makes it easily accessible from all major Scottish centres in less than two hours.

The Castle has known the splendour of Royal visitations, submitted to occupation by opposing forces on no less than four occasions, suffered siege and changed its architectural appearance to suit the taste of successive generations.

Today 32 rooms of infinite variety display beautiful furniture, fine collections of paintings, arms, armour, china, costumes, lace and embroidery, masonic regalia, Jacobite relics and other unique treasures giving a stirring picture of Scottish life from the 16th to 20th centuries.

The Duke of Atholl has the unique distinction of having the only remaining Private Army in Europe - The Atholl Highlanders.

GARDENS

Blair Castle is set in extensive parklands. Near the car and coach parks, there is a picnic area, a deer park and a unique two acre plantation of large trees known as 'Diana's Grove.' It has been said that "it is unlikely that any other two acres in the world contain such a number of different conifers of such heights and of such small age." A restored 18th century garden re-opened to visitors in 1996.

CONTACT

Geoff G Crerar
Tourism Administrator
Blair Castle
Blair Atholl
Pitlochry
Perthshire
PH18 5TL

Tel: (01796) 481207

Fax: (01796) 481487

LOCATION

OS Ref. NN880 660

From Edinburgh 80m, M90 to Perth, A9, follow signs for Blair Castle. 1½ hrs. Trunk Road A9 2m.

Bus: Bus stop 1m in Blair Atholl.

Train: 1m, Blair Atholl Euston-Inverness line.

Taxi: Elizabeth Yule, (01796) 472290.

OPENING TIMES

SUMMER
27 March - 31 October daily, 10am - 6pm
Last admission 5pm.

WINTER
Closed from
1 November - 31 March.

ADMISSION

House

Adult	£5.50
Child/Student**	£4.00
OAP	£4.50
Family	£15.00
Disabled	£2.00

Groups*

Adult	£5.00
Child/Student**	£4.00
OAP	£4.50
Disabled	£2.00

*   Minimum payment £200 out of season.

** (Age 5 - 16yrs)

Grounds & Parking

Cars	£2.00
Mini Buses	£5.00
Coaches*	£10.00

*unless booked

SPECIAL EVENTS

- **MAY 24:**
  Atholl Highlanders' Parade

- **MAY 25:**
  Atholl Gathering & Highland Games

- **NOV:**
  Glenfiddich World Piping Championships

FUNCTION		
ROOM	SIZE	MAX CAPACITY
Ballroom	89' x 35'	400
State Dining Rm	36' x 25'	200
Library	27' x 15'	40

ℹ️ Fashion shows, archery, clay pigeon shooting, garden parties, equestrian events, shows, rallies, filming, highland and charity balls, piping championships, grand piano, helicopter pad, cannon firing by Atholl Highlanders, resident piper, needlework displays. No smoking.

✖️ Buffets, dinners, wedding receptions and banquets.

♿ Visitors may alight at the entrance. WC and wheelchair.

☕ Two restaurants (no smoking) for tea, snacks and lunches.

🚶 In English, German and French at no extra cost. Max group size 25, tour time 1½ hrs.

🅿️ 200 cars, 20 coaches. Coach drivers and couriers free, plus free meal and free prize draw, information pack.

👨‍👩‍👧 Welcome, £4 each, primary schools £3 each. Nature walks, deer park, children's games, pony trekking.

🐕 No dogs.

GLAMIS CASTLE
Glamis

GLAMIS CASTLE is the family home of the Earls of Strathmore and Kinghorne and has been a royal residence since 1372. It is the childhood home of Her Majesty Queen Elizabeth The Queen Mother, the birthplace of Her Royal Highness The Princess Margaret and the legendary setting of Shakespeare's play *Macbeth*. Though the Castle is open to visitors it remains a family home lived in and loved by the Strathmore family.

The castle, a five-storey 'L' shaped tower block, was originally a royal hunting lodge. It was remodelled in the 17th century and is built of pink sandstone. It contains the Great Hall,

with its magnificent plasterwork ceiling dated 1621, a beautiful family Chapel constructed inside the Castle in 1688, an 18th century billiard room housing what is left of the extensive library once at Glamis, a 19th century dining room containing family portraits and the Royal Apartments which have been used by Her Majesty Queen Elizabeth The Queen Mother.

The castle stands in an extensive park, landscaped towards the end of the 18th Century, and contains the beautiful Italian Garden which reflects the peace and serenity of the castle and grounds.

CONTACT

Lt Col P J Cardwell Moore
(The Administrator)
Estates Office
Glamis Castle
Glamis
By Forfar
Angus
DD8 1RJ

Tel: (01307) 840393

Fax: (01307) 840733

LOCATION

OS Ref. NO386 480

From Edinburgh M90, A94, 81m.
From Forfar A94, 6m.
From Glasgow 101m.

Motorway: M90.

Rail: Dundee Station 12m.

Air: Dundee Airport 12m.

Taxi: B Morrison (01575) 572988.

CONFERENCE/FUNCTION		
ROOM	SIZE	MAX CAPACITY
Dining Rm	84 sq.m.	120
Restaurant	140 sq.m.	100

i Shopping complex. Fashion shoots, archery, clay pigeon shooting, equestrian events, shows, rallies, filming, product launches, highland games, new cricket pavilion, grand piano. No photography in the castle.

The State Rooms are available for grand dinners, lunches and wedding receptions.

Disabled visitors may alight at entrance. Those in wheelchairs will be unable to tour the castle but may visit the two exhibitions. WC.

Self-service, licensed restaurant. Morning coffees, light lunches, afternoon teas.

All visits are guided, tour time 50 - 60 mins. Tours leave every 10 - 15 mins. Tours in French, German, Italian and Spanish by appointment at no additional cost. Three exhibitions.

P 500 cars and 20 coaches. Coach drivers and couriers admitted free. Beware narrow gates; they are wide enough to take buses (10ft wide).

Welcome, one teacher free for every 10 children. Nature trail, family exhibition rooms, dolls house, play park. Glamis Heritage Education Centre in Glamis village. Education pack.

OPENING TIMES

SUMMER

28 March - 26 October
Daily, 10.30am - 5.30pm.

July - August
opens 10am

Last admission 4.45pm.

WINTER

Groups welcome, by appointment.

ADMISSION

SUMMER

House & Garden

Adult	£5.00
Child (Under 16)	£2.60
OAP/Student	£3.80
Family	£13.50

Groups (min 20 people)	
Adult	£4.50
Child (under 16)	£2.30
OAP/Student	£3.30

Garden only

Adult	£2.30
Child (under 16)	£1.20
OAP	£1.20
Disabled	FREE

Groups (min 20 people)	
Adult	£2.30
Child (under 16)	£1.20
OAP	£1.20

WINTER

By arrangement.

SPECIAL EVENTS

• **JUL:**
The 24th Scottish Transport Extravaganza, presented by Strathmore Vintage Vehicle Club Ltd.

• **JUL:**
A Grand Scottish Prom, The National Symphony Orchestra of Scotland, outdoor picnic concert with spectacular firework finale

• **AUG:**
Craft Fair

SCONE PALACE
Perth

SCONE PALACE, just outside Perth, is the home of the Earls of Mansfield. Here Kenneth MacAlpine united Scotland and in 838AD, placed the stone of Scone upon the Moot Hill which became the Crowning Place of Scottish Kings, including Macbeth and Robert the Bruce. Edward I moved the Coronation Stone to Westminster in 1296.

The Abbey of Scone and the Bishops' Palace were ransacked and burned in 1559. The Gowries built a new Palace in 1580, which was enlarged and embellished around 1804 by the Third Earl and houses a fabulous collection of French furniture, clocks, 16th Century needlework (including bed hangings worked by Mary Queen of Scots),

ivories, objets d'art and Vernis Martin and one of the finest collections of porcelain in the country.

GARDENS

Scone's famous pinetum is a unique collection of rare pines, some of which are over 150 feet high and still growing. There are pleasant walks through 100 acres of wild garden which offer the visitor magnificent displays of daffodils, rhododendrons and azaleas.

There is a fine picnic area, adventure playground and a collection of veteran machinery. A cricket pitch and pavilion in an attractive setting is ideal for a variety of outdoor functions.

❖

CONTACT

The Administrator
Scone Palace
Perth
PH2 6BD

Tel: (01738) 552300

Fax: (01738) 552588

LOCATION

OS Ref. NO114 266

From Edinburgh Forth Bridge M90, A93 1 hr.

Bus: 2 buses a day from Perth.

Rail: Perth Station 3m.

Motorway: M90 from Edinburgh.

Taxi: Perth Radio Cabs (01738) 628171.

OPENING TIMES

SUMMER
28 March - 13 October
daily: 9.30am - 5pm.

Evening tours by appointment.

WINTER
14 October - 9 April
By appointment only.

ADMISSION

SUMMER
Palace & Garden
Adult £5.00
Child* £2.80
OAP.......................£4.20
Family £15.00
Groups (min. 20)
Adult £4.50
Child* £2.50
OAP......................£3.90

Garden only
Adult £2.50
Child* £1.40

*Age 5 - 16

WINTER
Per person.................£9.00
(£180 min. payment)

CONFERENCE/FUNCTION		
ROOM	SIZE	MAX CAPACITY
Long Gallery	140' x 20'	250
Queen Victoria's Rm	20' x 20'	35
Drawing Rm	50' x 24'	100

i Shop. Receptions, fashion shows, war games, archery, clay pigeon shooting, equestrian events, garden parties, shows, rallies, filming, shooting, fishing, floodlit tattoos, product launches, highland games, parkland, cricket pitch, airfield, helicopter landing, croquet, speciality lectures, racecourse, polo field, firework displays, adventure playground.

X Grand dinners in state rooms, buffets, receptions, wedding receptions, cocktail parties.

All state rooms on one level, wheelchair access to restaurants. Visitors may alight at entrance. WC.

Two restaurants, teas, lunches, dinners, can be booked, menus upon request, special rates for groups.

Free, guides in rooms, tour time 45 mins. French and German guides available by appointment.

P 500 cars and 15 coaches, groups please book, couriers and coach drivers free meal and admittance. Last visit of season token for couriers of booked groups.

ABERDOUR CASTLE

Tel: 01383 860519

Aberdour, Fife

Owner: Historic Scotland   **Contact:** The Custodian

A 14th century castle built by the Douglas family. The gallery on the first floor gives an idea of how it was furnished at the time. The castle has a 14th century tower extended in the 16th and 17th centuries, a delightful walled garden and a circular dovecote.

Location: OS Ref. NT193 854. In Aberdour 5m E of the Forth Bridge on the A921.

Opening Times: 1 Apr - 30 Sept: Mon - Sat, 9.30am - 6.30pm, Sun, 2 - 6.30pm, last ticket 6pm. 1 Oct - 31 Mar: Mon - Sat, 9.30am - 4.30pm, Sun, 2 - 4.30pm, last ticket 4pm. Closed Thur pm and Fri in winter.

Admission: Adult £1.50, Conc. £1, Child 75p.

ANGUS FOLK MUSEUM

A Forbes

KIRKWYND, GLAMIS, FORFAR, ANGUS DD8 1RT

Owner: *The National Trust For Scotland*   **Contact:** *Isla MacLeod*

Tel: 01307 840288

Where will you find cruisie lamps, pirn winders, cloutie rugs, bannock spades and a thrawcrook? In these fascinating items, and many more, are to be found in the Angus Folk Museum, one of Scotland's finest. The domestic section is housed in six charming 19th century cottages in Kirk Wynd, and the agricultural collection is in the farm steading opposite. The displays inside the building explain and illustrate changes in the Angus countryside in the last 200 years.

Location: OS Ref. NO385 467. Off A94, in Glamis, 5m SW of Forfar.

Opening Times: Good Fri - Easter Mon, 1 May - 30 Sept; daily, 11am - 5pm. Weekends in Oct: 11am - 5pm, last admission 4.30pm.

Admission: Adult £2.30, Child £1.50, Family £6.10. Groups: Adult £1.80, School £1.

i Shop.   House suitable. WC.   **P** Limited.   No dogs.

ARBROATH ABBEY

Tel: 01241 878756

Arbroath, Tayside

Owner: Historic Scotland   **Contact:** The Custodian

The substantial ruins of a Tironensian monastery, notably the gate house range and the abbot's house. Arbroath Abbey holds a very special place in Scottish history. It was here in 1320 that Scotland's nobles swore their independence from England in the famous 'Declaration of Arbroath'.

Location: OS Ref. NO644 414. In Arbroath town centre on the A92.

Opening Times: 1 Apr - 30 Sept: Mon - Sat 9.30am - 6.30pm, Sun 2 - 6.30pm. Last ticket 6pm. 1 Oct - 31 Mar: Mon - Sat, 9.30am - 4.30 pm, Sun 2 - 4.30pm. Last ticket 4pm.

Admission: Adult £1.50, Conc. 75p, Child 75p.

BARRIE'S BIRTHPLACE

Tel: 01575 572646

9 Brechin Road, Kirriemuir, Angus DD8 4BX

Owner: The National Trust for Scotland   **Contact:** Karen Gilmour or Mrs Sheila Philp

'Do you believe in fairies? The creator of the eternal magic of *Peter Pan*, J M Barrie, was born here in 1860. He was the ninth of ten children born to David Barrie, a handloom weaver and his wife Margaret Ogilvy. See the imaginative exhibition about this famous novelist and dramatist with life-size figures, miniature stage sets, dioramas, theatre posters and stage costumes, while a darting light, 'Tinkerbell', moves around the room!

Location: OS Ref. NO388 542. On A926/B957, in Kirriemuir, 6m NW of Forfar.

Opening Times: Good Fri - Easter Mon, 1 May - 30 Sept: Mon - Sat 11am - 5.30pm, Sun 1.30 - 5.30pm. Weekends in Oct: Sat 11am - 5.30pm, Sun 1.30pm - 5.30pm, last adm. 5pm.

Admission: Adult £1.80, Child £1.20, Family £4.80. Groups: Adult £1.50, School £1.

Stairlift.   Tearoom.   **P** No parking.   No dogs.

BARRY MILL

Tel: 01241 856761

Barry, Carnoustie, Angus DD7 7RJ

Owner: The National Trust for Scotland   **Contact:** Peter Ellis

18th & 19th century meal mill. Demonstrations and displays. Waymarked walks. Picnic area.

Location: OS Ref. NO533 349. N of village between A92 & A930, 2m W of Carnoustie.

Opening Times: Good Fri - Easter Mon, 1 May - 30 Sept; daily, 11am - 5pm. Weekends in Oct: 11am - 5pm.

Admission: Adult £1.80, Child £1.20, Family £4.80. Groups: Adult £1.50, School £1.

BLAIR CASTLE

See page 35 for full page entry.

BOLFRACKS GARDEN

Tel: 01887 820207

Aberfeldy, Perthshire PH15 2EX

Owner: Mr J D Hutchison   **Contact:** Mr J D Hutchison

A garden for all seasons overlooking the Tay Valley. Approximately 4 acres with a walled garden including a good collection of roses and walks along the burn garden with rhododendrons, azaleas, meconopsis and primulas.

Location: OS Ref. NN822 481. 2m W of Aberfeldy on A827 towards Kenmore.

Opening Times: 1 Apr - 31 Oct; daily, 10am - 6pm.

Admission: Adult £2, Child (under 16 years) free.

No dogs.

BRANKLYN GARDEN

Tel: 01738 625535

Dundee Road, Perth PH2 7BB

Owner: The National Trust for Scotland   **Contact:** Steve McNamara

Here is a small but magnificent garden with an impressive collection of rare and unusual plants. Among the most breathtaking is the Himalayan blue poppy, *Meconopsis X Sheldonii*. There is a rock garden with purple maple and the rare golden *Cedrus*. Seasonal highlights in May and June are the alpines and rhododendrons and in autumn the fiery red *Acer palmatum*.

Location: OS Ref. NO125 225. On A85 at 116 Dundee Road, Perth.

Opening Times: 1 Mar - 31 Oct; daily, 9.30am - sunset.

Admission: Adult £2.30, Child £1.50, Family £6.10. Groups: Adult £1.80, School £1.

i Shop, plant centre.   Grounds suitable, but limited access.   No dogs.

CAMBO GARDENS

Tel: 01333 450654   **Fax:** 01333 450987

Cambo Estate, Kingsbarns, St Andrews, Fife KY16 8QD

Owner: Peter Erskine Esq   **Contact:** Catherine Erskine

Enchanting traditional walled garden in bloom from snowdrops to Autumn crocus. Blossoms, bulbs, lilies and 200 varieties of roses are a speciality. Gardened with joy to make it more fun than fossilised.

Location: OS Ref. NO603 114. 3m N of Crail. 7m SE of St Andrews.

Opening Times: All year; daily except Christmas and New Year 10am - 4pm.

Admission: Adult £2, Child free.

i Conferences.   Not suitable.   In grounds, on leads.   **A** Available.

CASTLE MENZIES

Tel: 01887 820982

Weem, Aberfeldy, Perth PH15 2JD

Owner: Menzies Charitable Trust   **Contact:** R A Adam

Seat of Chiefs of Clan Menzies. 16th century fortified house. Bonnie Prince Charlie rested here en route for Culloden in 1746.

Location: OS Ref. NN838 497. 1^1/2 m from Aberfeldy on B846.

Opening Times: 1 Apr - 12 Oct.

Admission: Adult £2.50, Child £1, Conc. £2, Groups: Adult £2.25.

i Shop.   Ground floor suitable. WC.   Tearoom.   Guide dogs in grounds.

CHARLETON HOUSE

Tel: 01333 340249   **Fax:** 01333 340583

Colinsburgh, Leven, Fife KY9 1HG

Location: OS Ref. NO464 036. Off A917. 1m NW of Colinsburgh. 3m NW of Elie.

Opening Times: Sept: 12 - 3pm. Admission every ^{1}/2 hr with guided tours only.

Admission: Standard £5.

CLUNY HOUSE GARDENS

Tel: 01887 820795

Aberfeldy, Perthshire PH15 2JT

Contact: W Mattingley

Good woodland garden including many rare Himalayan species.

Location: OS Ref. NN879 513. 3^1/2 m NW of Aberfeldy on the Weem to Strathtay Road.

Opening Times: 1 Mar - 31 Oct: 10am - 6pm.

Admission: Adult £2, Child under 16 free, Groups: £2 per person (guided tour).

i Plant centre.   Not suitable.   By arrangement.   **P** Limited.   No dogs.

CULROSS PALACE

CULROSS, FIFE KY12 8JH

Owner: *The National Trust For Scotland*   **Contact:** *Michael Ford*

Tel: 01383 880359

Relive the domestic life of the 16th and 17th centuries at this Royal Burgh fringed by the River Forth. Here the old buildings and cobbled streets create a time warp for visitors as they explore the old town. Enjoy too the Palace, dating from 1597 and the medieval garden.

Location: OS Ref. NS985 860. Off A985. 12m W of Forth Road Bridge and 4m E of Kincardine Bridge, Fife.

Opening Times: Palace: 28 Mar (Good Fri) - 30 Sept; daily 11am - 5pm, last admission 4pm. Town house & study: same dates, 1.30 - 5pm and weekends in Oct: 11am - 5pm. Groups other times by appointment. Tearoom (in Bessie Bar Hall) dates as Town house, 10.30am - 4.30pm.

Admission: Adult £4, Child £2.70, Family £10.70. Groups: Adult £3.20, School £1.

WC.   Tearoom.   By arrangement.   Ample.   No dogs.

DRUMMOND CASTLE GARDENS

MUTHILL, CRIEFF, PERTHSHIRE PH5 2AA

Owner: *Grimsthorpe & Drummond Castle Trust*   **Contact:** *Joe Buchanan*

Tel: 01764 681257 **Fax:** 01764 681550

Scotland's most important formal gardens, among the finest in Europe. The terraces overlook a magnificent parterre, celebrating the saltire and family heraldry, surrounding the famous multiplex sundial by John Milne, Master Mason to Charles I. Featured in the United Artists' film *Rob Roy.*

Location: OS Ref. NN844 181. 2m S of Crieff off the A822.

Opening Times: Easter then 1 May - 31 Oct: 2 - 6pm, last entry 5pm.

Admission: Adult £3, Child £1.50, OAP £2.

Partially suitable.   Coach parties must book.   In grounds, on leads.

SPECIAL EVENTS
AUG 3: Open Day, 2 - 6pm, entertainments, teas, raffle.

DAMSIDE HERB GARDEN   **Tel:** 01561 361496

Montrose, Angus, Kincardine DD10 0HY

Owner: Ian Cruickshank   **Contact:** Ian Cruickshank

Location: OS Ref. NO786 703. Signposted on A92 halfway between Stonehaven and Montrose.

Opening Times: Daily, 10am - 5pm. Closed Jan & Feb.

Admission: Adult £1, Child 80p, Conc. 80p, accompanied child under 12 free. Groups by arrangement.

Colonel Wm. Gordon of Fyvie Castle, by Batoni.

DUNFERMLINE ABBEY & PALACE   **Tel:** 01383 739026

Dunfermline, Fife

Owner: Historic Scotland   **Contact:** The Custodian

The remains of the Benedictine abbey founded by Queen Margaret in the 11th century. The foundations of her church are under the 12th century Romanesque-style nave. Robert the Bruce was buried in the choir. Substantial parts of the Abbey buildings remain, including the vast refectory.

Location: OS Ref. NY090 873. In Dunfermline off the M90.

Opening Times: 1 Apr - 30 Sept: Mon - Sat, 9.30am - 6.30pm, Sun, 2 - 6.30pm, last ticket 6pm. 1 Oct - 31 Mar: Mon - Sat, 9.30am - 4.30pm, Sun, 2 - 4.30pm, last ticket 4pm. Closed Thur pm and Fri in winter.

Admission: Adult £1.50, Conc. £1, Child 75p.

EDZELL CASTLE AND GARDEN   **Tel:** 01356 648631

Edzell, Angus

Owner: Historic Scotland   **Contact:** The Custodian

The beautiful walled garden at Edzell is one of Scotland's unique sights, created by Sir David Lindsay in 1604. The 'Pleasance' is a delightful formal garden with walls decorated with sculptured stone panels, flower boxes and niches for nesting birds. The fine tower house, now ruined, dates from the last years of the 15th century. Mary Queen of Scots held a council meeting in the castle in 1562 on her way north as her army marched against the Gordons.

Location: OS Ref. NO585 691. At Edzell, 6m N of Brechin on B966. 1m W of village.

Opening Times: 1 Apr - 30 Sept: Mon - Sat, 9.30am - 6.30pm, Sun, 2 - 6.30pm, last ticket 6pm. 1 Oct - 31 Mar: Mon - Sat, 9.30am - 4.30pm, Sun, 2 - 4.30pm, last ticket 4pm. Closed Thur pm and Fri in winter.

Admission: Adult £2.30, Conc. £1.50, Child £1.

ELCHO CASTLE   **Tel:** 0131 668 8800

Perth

Owner: Historic Scotland

This handsome and complete fortified mansion of 16th century date has four projecting towers. The original wrought-iron grilles to protect the windows are still in place.

Location: OS Ref. NO164 211. On the Tay, 3m SE of Perth.

Opening Times: Tel: 0131 668 8800 for details.

Admission: Adult £1.50, Conc. £1, Child 75p.

FALKLAND PALACE

Douglas MacGregor

FALKLAND KY15 7BU

Owner: The National Trust for Scotland   *Contact:* Mrs Margaret Marshall

Tel: 01337 857397

The Royal Palace of Falkland, set in the heart of a unique medieval village, was the country residence and hunting lodge of eight Stuart monarchs, including Mary, Queen of Scots. Built between 1502 and 1541, the Palace is an extremely fine example of Renaissance architecture. It includes the exceptionally beautiful Chapel Royal, and is surrounded by internationally known gardens, laid out in the 1950s. The Royal Tennis Court, reputedly the world's oldest, is still used today.

Location: OS Ref. NO253 075. A912, 11m N of Kirkcaldy.

Opening Times: Palace & garden: 28 Mar (Good Fri) - 31 Oct: Mon - Sat 11am - 5.30pm, Sun 1.30 - 5.30pm, last admission to palace 4.30pm, to garden 5pm. Groups at other times by appointment. Town Hall by appointment only.

Admission: Adult £4.50, Child £3. Groups: Adult £3.60, School £1. Family £12. Garden only: Adult £2.30, Child £1.50. Groups: Adult £1.80, School £1.

i Shop.	Grounds suitable.	No dogs.

HILL OF TARVIT MANSIONHOUSE

CUPAR, FIFE KY15 5PB

Owner: The National Trust for Scotland   *Contact:* Mrs June Pratt

Tel: 01334 653127

This fine house was rebuilt in 1906 by Sir Robert Lorimer, the renowned Scottish architect, for a Dundee industrialist, Mr F B Sharp. The house still presents a perfect setting for Mr Sharp's notable collection of superb French, Chippendale and vernacular furniture. Fine paintings by Raeburn and Ramsay and a number of eminent Dutch artists are on view together with Chinese porcelain and bronzes. Don't miss the restored Edwardian laundry behind the house which is set in the midst of a delightful garden.

Location: OS Ref. NO379 118. Off A916, 2¹⁄₂ m S of Cupar, Fife.

Opening Times: House: Good Fri - Easter Mon & 1 May - 30 Sept: daily, 1.30 - 5.30pm. Weekends in Oct: 1.30 - 5.30pm, last admission 4.45pm. Tearoom: same dates but opens 12.30pm. Garden & grds: All year, daily, 9.30am - sunset.

Admission: Adult £3.50, Child £2.30, Family £9.30. Groups: Adult £2.80, School £1.

i Shop.	Ground floor & grounds suitable.	Tearoom.
By arrangement.	*P* Ample.	No dogs.

GLAMIS CASTLE   See page 36 for full page entry.

GLENEAGLES   **Tel:** 01764 682388

Auchterarder, Perthshire PH3 1PJ

Owner: Gleneagles 1996 Trust   **Contact:** J Martin Haldane of Gleneagles

Gleneagles had been the home of the Haldane family since the 12th century. The 18th century pavilion is open to the public by written appointment.

Location: OS Ref. NS930 088. Auchterarder.

Opening Times: By written appointment only.

House of Dun, Angus.

HOUSE OF DUN

Harvey Wood

MONTROSE, ANGUS DD10 9LQ

Owner: The National Trust for Scotland   *Contact:* David Sharland

Tel: 01674 810264   **Fax:** 01674 810722

This beautiful Georgian house, overlooking the Montrose Basin, was designed by William Adam and built in 1730 for David Erskine, Lord Dun. Lady Augusta Kennedy-Erskine was the natural daughter of William IV and Mrs Jordan and House of Dun contains many royal mementos. The house features superb plasterwork by Joseph Enzer.

Location: OS Ref. NO670 599. 3m W Montrose on A935.

Opening Times: House & shop: Good Fri - Easter Mon, 1 May - 30 Sept; daily, 1.30 - 5.30pm. Weekends in Oct: 1.30 - 5.30pm, last admission 5pm. Restaurant: same dates but opens 12.30pm. Garden & grounds: all year, daily 9.30am - sunset.

Admission: Adult £3.50, Child £2.30, Family £9.30. Groups: Adult £2.80, School £1. Gardens & grounds: Honesty box £1.

i Shop. Conferences.	Ground floor & basement suitable. WC.
Restaurant.	In grounds, on leads. Special dog walk.

HOUSE OF PITMUIES

GUTHRIE BY FORFAR, ANGUS DD8 2SD

Owner: *Mrs Farquhar Ogilvie*   ***Contact:*** *Mrs Farquhar Ogilvie*

Tel: 01241 828245

Semi-formal walled gardens celebrated for their delphiniums, rose collection and herbaceous borders in summer. Cool woodland and riverside walks with fine trees and massed spring bulbs. Fine 18th century house (open by appointment) flanked by stone-roofed outbuildings with adjacent 'Gothick' wash house and unique turreted doo-cot.

Location: OS Ref. NO567 500. A932, $6^{1}/_{2}$ m E of Forfar, 8m NW of Arbroath, $1^{1}/_{2}$ m W of Friockheim.

Opening Times: Easter - 31 Oct: daily, 10am - 5pm.

Admission: Garden: Adult £2, Child (under 12) free. Free parking.

☕ Available for pre-booked groups.   🐄 In grounds, on leads.

KELLIE CASTLE & GARDEN

Douglas MacGregor

PITTENWEEM, FIFE KY10 2RF

Owner: *The National Trust for Scotland*   ***Contact:*** *Mr John Oatts*

Tel: 01333 720271

This very fine example of domestic architecture in Lowland Scotland dates from the 14th century and was sympathetically restored by the Lorimer family in the late 19th century. The castle contains magnificent plaster ceilings and painted panelling as well as fine furniture designed by Sir Robert Lorimer. Of particular interest are the Victorian nursery and the old kitchen. The late Victorian garden features a fine collection of old fashioned roses and herbaceous plants which are cultivated organically.

Location: OS Ref. NO519 051. On B9171, 3m NW of Pittenweem, Fife.

Opening Times: Castle: Good Fri - Easter Mon & 1 May - 30 Sept: daily, 1.30 - 5.30pm. Weekends in Oct: 1.30 - 5.30pm, last admission 4.45pm. Garden & grounds: All year, daily, 9.30am - sunset.

Admission: Adult £3.50, Child £2.30, Family £9.30. Groups: Adult £2.80, School £1.

ℹ️ Shop.   ♿ Ground floor & grounds suitable.   🐄 No dogs.

HUNTINGTOWER CASTLE   Tel: 01738 627231

Perth

Owner: Historic Scotland   **Contact:** The Custodian

The splendid painted ceilings are especially noteworthy in this castle, once owned by the Ruthven family. Scene of a famous leap between two towers by a daughter of the house who was nearly caught in her lover's room. The two towers are still complete, one of 15th - 16th century date, the other of 16th century origin. Now linked by a 17th century range.

Location: OS Ref. NO084 252. 3m NW of Perth off the A85.

Opening Times: 1 Apr - 30 Sept: Mon - Sat, 9.30am - 6.30pm, Sun, 2 - 6.30pm, last ticket 6pm. 1 Oct - 31 Mar: Mon - Sat, 9.30am - 4.30pm, Sun, 2 - 4.30pm, last ticket 4pm. Closed Thur pm and Fri in winter.

Admission: Adult £1.50, Conc. £1, Child 75p.

INCHCOLM ABBEY   Tel: 01383 823332

Inchcolm, Fife

Owner: Historic Scotland   **Contact:** The Custodian

Known as the 'Iona of the East'. This is the best preserved group of monastic buildings in Scotland, founded in 1123. Includes a 13th century octagonal chapter house.

Location: OS Ref. NT190 826. On Inchcolm in the Firth of Forth. Reached by ferry from South Queensferry (30 mins) tel. 0131 331 4857, and from North Queensferry (weather permitting).

Opening Times: 1 Apr - 30 Sept: Mon - Sat 9.30am - 6.30pm, Sun 2 - 6.30pm. Last ticket 6pm.

Admission: Adult £2.30, Conc. £1.50, Child £1. Additional charge for ferries.

LOCH LEVEN CASTLE   Tel: 01786 450000

Loch Leven, Kinross

Owner: Historic Scotland   **Contact:** The Regional Custodian

Mary Queen of Scots endured nearly a year of imprisonment in this 14th century tower before her dramatic escape in May 1568. During the First War of Independence it was held by the English, stormed by Wallace and visited by Bruce.

Location: OS Ref. NO138 018. On island in Loch Leven reached by ferry from Kinross off the M90.

Opening Times: 1 Apr - 30 Sept: Mon - Sat 9.30am - 6.30pm, Sun 2 - 6.30pm. Last ticket 6pm.

Admission: Adult £2.80, Conc. £1.80, Child £1. Prices include ferry trip.

Kellie Castle, Fife.

MEGGINCH CASTLE GARDENS
Tel: 01821 642222 **Fax:** 01821 642708

Errol, Perthshire PH2 7SW

Owner: Captain Drummond of Megginch and Lady Strange

15th century castle, 1,000 year old yews, flowered parterre, double walled kitchen garden, topiary, astrological garden, pagoda dovecote in courtyard. Part used as a location for the film *Rob Roy* released in 1995.

Location: OS Ref. NO241 245. 8m E of Perth on A90.

Opening Times: Apr - Oct: Wed. Aug: daily 2.30 - 6pm.

Admission: Adult £2.50, Child £1.

MEIGLE SCULPTURED STONE MUSEUM
Tel: 01828 640612

Meigle

Owner: Historic Scotland

A remarkable collection of 25 sculptured monuments of the Celtic Christian period. This is one of the finest collections of Dark Age sculpture in Western Europe.

Location: OS Ref. NO287 446. In Meigle on the A94.

Opening Times: 1 Apr - 30 Sept: Mon - Sat 9.30am - 6.30pm. Sun 2 - 6.30pm. Last ticket 6pm.

Admission: Adult £1.50, Conc. £1, Child 75p.

MONZIE CASTLE
Tel: 01764 653110

Crieff, Perthshire PH7 4HD

Owner: Mrs C M M Crichton **Contact:** Mrs C M M Crichton

Built in 1791. Destroyed by fire in 1908 and rebuilt and furnished by Sir Robert Lorimer.

Location: OS Ref. NN873 244. 2m NE of Crieff.

Opening Times: 17 May - 15 Jun: daily, 2 - 5pm. By appointment at other times.

Admission: Adult £3, Child £1. Groups: Adult £2.50, Child 50p.

ST ANDREWS CASTLE
Tel: 01334 477196

St Andrews, Fife

Owner: Historic Scotland **Contact:** The Custodian

The ruins of the castle of the Archbishops of St Andrews. An exhibition in the visitor centre brings the history of the castle and the cathedral to life.

Location: OS Ref. NO513 169. In St Andrews on the A91.

Opening Times: 1 Apr - 30 Sept: Mon - Sat 9.30am - 6.30pm, Sun 2 - 6.30pm. Last ticket 6pm. 1 Oct - 31 Mar: Mon - Sat 9.30am - 4.30pm, Sun 2 - 4.30pm. Last ticket 4pm.

Admission: Adult £2.30, Conc. £1.50, Child £1. Joint entry ticket with St Andrews Cathedral: Adult £3.30, Conc. £2, Child £1.25.

ST ANDREWS CATHEDRAL
Tel: 01334 472563

St Andrews, Fife

Owner: Historic Scotland **Contact:** The Administrator

The remains still give a vivid impression of the scale of what was once the largest cathedral in Scotland along with the associated domestic ranges of the priory. The precinct walls are particularly well preserved. Climb St Rule's Tower for a magnificent view of the town and visit the cathedral's collection of celtic and medieval carved stones and other relics found on the site.

Location: OS Ref: NO514 167. In St Andrews.

Opening Times: 1 Apr - 30 Sept: Mon - Sat 9.30am - 6.30pm, Sun 2 - 6.30pm. Last ticket 6pm. 1 Oct - 31 Mar: Mon - Sat 9.30am - 4.30pm, Sun 2 - 4.30pm. Last ticket 4pm.

Admission: Adult £1.50, Conc. £1, Child 75p. Joint entry ticket available with St Andrews Castle: Adult £3.30, Conc. £2, Child £1.25.

SCONE PALACE
See page 37 for full page entry.

SCOTLAND'S SECRET BUNKER
Tel: 01333 310301 **Fax:** 01333 312040

Troywood, St Andrews KY16 8QH **Contact:** General Manager

100ft under ground is the secret bunker where the Government would have gone in the event of a nuclear war. Operations room. Cinemas. Restaurants. An unique family day out.

Location: OS Ref. NO562 090. Off the B940, 6m S of St Andrews. Thistle signs.

Opening Times: 28 Mar (Good Fri) - 31 Oct: 11am - 6pm. Last admission at 5pm.

Admission: Adult £4.95, Conc. £3.95, Family £14. Evening curator's tours by arrangement.

Thirlestane Castle, Lauder (South of Scotland).

Manderston —the marble dairy (South of Scotland).

Drummond Castle Gardens (Perthshire).

BLAIRQUHAN CASTLE
Maybole

BLAIRQUHAN is the home of James Hunter Blair, the great great grandson of Sir David Hunter Blair, 3rd Baronet for whom it was designed by William Burn and built in 1821-24.

All the Regency furniture bought for the house remains, and the house has not been altered except discreetly to bring it up-to-date. There are ten double bedrooms including four four-poster beds, with en-suite bathrooms, five singles, and many public rooms which can be used for conferences and every sort of occasion.

The castle is approached by a 3 mile private drive along the River Girvan and is situated in one of the most charming parts of south west Scotland. There is a well-known collection of pictures. It is particularly suitable for conferences because the house is entirely at your disposal.

A five minute walk from the Castle are the walled gardens, laid out around the 1800s and recently replanned and replanted.

Blairquhan is only 50 miles from Glasgow. It is within about half an hour's drive of the world famous golf courses of Prestwick, Troon and Turnberry, the last two of which are venues for the British Open Golf Championships.

CONTACT

James Hunter Blair
Blairquhan Castle
Maybole
Ayrshire
KA19 7LZ

Tel: (01655) 770239

Fax: (01655) 770278

LOCATION

OS Ref. NS366 055

From London M6 to Carlisle, A75 to Crocketford, A712 to A713 nr New Galloway, B741 to Straiton, B7045 to Ayr. Turn left 1/4 m beyond village. 6m SE of Maybole off B7045.

Rail: Maybole 7m.

Air: Prestwick Airport, 15m. Direct flights to London, Belfast & Dublin. Executive Travel: contact (01655) 882666

OPENING TIMES

SUMMER
22 July - 17 August
daily except Mon
1.30 - 4.15pm
(last admission 4.15pm)

Open at all other times by appointment.

WINTER
Open by appointment.

ADMISSION

House & Garden

Adult £3.50
Child (5 - 14yrs)........£2.00
OAP.........................£2.50

Groups*
Negotiable

* Minimum payment £20.

SPECIAL EVENTS

- **JUL 22 - AUG 17:**
  Events every weekend - including archery and kite flying

- **AUG 2 / 3:**
  Battle re-enactment by The Civil War Society.

CONFERENCE/FUNCTION		
ROOM	SIZE	MAX CAPACITY
Drawing Rms	1200 sq ft	100
Dining Rm	750 sq ft	100
Library	400 sq ft	25
Saloon	600 sq ft	100
Meeting Rm	255 sq ft	50

i Shop. Fashion shows, air displays, archery, shooting, equestrian events, garden parties, shows, rallies, filming, grand piano, snooker, fishing. Slide projector, overhead projector, screen, and secretarial assistance for meetings. No photography in castle.

X Available. Wedding receptions.

Visitors may alight at the entrance. WC.

Restaurant, teas, lunches, buffets and dinners. Groups can book in advance, special rates for groups.

At no extra charge, up to 100, tour time 1hr, also available in French.

P Unlimited.

Welcome, guide and schoolroom provided, cost negotiable.

A 10 doubles (4 4-posters) with bathrooms en-suite, 5 singles. The Dower House at Milton has 8 doubles, 2 singles, 5 bathrooms. 7 holiday cottages on the Estate.

BOWHILL
Selkirk

Scottish Borders home of the Duke and Duchess of Buccleuch, dating mainly from 1812 and christened 'Sweet Bowhill' by Sir Walter Scott in his *Lay of the Last Minstrel.*

Many of the works of art were collected by earlier Montagus, Douglases and Scotts or given by Charles II to his natural son James Duke of Monmouth and Buccleuch. Paintings include Canaletto's *Whitehall*, works by Guardi, Claude, Ruysdael, Gainsborough, Raeburn, Reynolds, Van Dyck and Wilkie. Superb French furniture, Meissen and Sèvres porcelain, silver and tapestries.

Historical relics include Monmouth's saddle and execution shirt, Sir Walter Scott's plaid and some proof editions, Queen Victoria's letters and gifts to successive Duchesses of Buccleuch, her Mistresses of the Robes.

There is also a completely restored Victorian Kitchen, 19th century horse-drawn fire engine, 'Bowhill Little Theatre', a lively centre for the performing arts and where, prior to touring the house, visitors can see 'The Quest for Bowhill', a 20 minute audio-visual by Dr Colin Thompson.

Conference centre, arts courses, education service, visitor centre. Shop, tearoom, adventure playground, woodland walks, nature trails, picnic areas. Garden and landscape designed by John Gilpin.

CONTACT

Mrs M Carter
Buccleuch Heritage Trust
Bowhill House &
Country Park
Bowhill
Selkirk
TD7 5ET

Tel: (01750) 22204

Fax: (01750) 22204

LOCATION

OS Ref. NT426 278

3m W of Selkirk off A708
Moffat Road,
A68 from Newcastle,
A7 from Carlisle
or Edinburgh.

Bus: 3m Selkirk.

Taxi: (01750) 20354.

i Shop. Fashion shows, air displays, archery, clay pigeon shooting, equestrian events, charity garden parties, shows, rallies, filming, lecture theatre. House is open by appointment outside public hours to groups led by officials of a recognised museum, gallery or educational establishment. No photography inside house.

✗ Inside caterers normally used but outside caterers considered.

♿ Visitors may alight at entrance. WC. Wheelchair visitors free.

☕ Restaurant. Parties can book in advance, special rates for groups, menus on request.

🚶 Available for groups. Tour time 1¼ hrs.

🅿 60 cars and 6 coaches within 50yds of house.

👪 Welcome. Projects in Bowhill House and Victorian kitchen, Education Officers (service provided free of charge), schoolroom, ranger-led nature walks, adventure playground.

CONFERENCE/FUNCTION

ROOM	SIZE	MAX CAPACITY
Bowhill Little Theatre		72

OPENING TIMES

SUMMER
26 April - late Summer BH (UK)

Country Park
Daily except Fri
(open Fri in July)
12 - 5pm.

House
July only.
daily: 1 - 4.30pm.

WINTER
By appointment only, for educational groups.

ADMISSION

SUMMER

House & Country Park
Adult £4.00
Child (5 - 16yrs)..........£1.00
OAP/Student..........£3.50
Group (min. 20).........£3.50

Country Park only
All ages......................£1.00

WINTER

House & Country Park
Adult £4.50
Child (5 - 16yrs)..........£1.00

Pre-booked educational groups over 20 persons welcomed.

DRUMLANRIG CASTLE
Thornhill

DRUMLANRIG CASTLE, Gardens and Country Park, the home of the Duke of Buccleuch and Queensberry KT was built between 1679 and 1691 by William Douglas, 1st Duke of Queensberry. Drumlanrig is rightly recognised as one of the first and most important buildings in the grand manner in Scottish domestic architecture. James Smith, who made the conversion from a 15th century castle, made a comparable transformation at Dalkeith a decade later.

The castle, of local pink sandstone offers superb views across Nithsdale. It houses a renowned art collection, including work by Leonardo, Holbein, and Rembrandt, as well as cabinets made for Louis XIV's Versailles, relics of Bonny Prince Charlie and a 300 year old silver chandelier.

The story of Sir James Douglas, killed in Spain while carrying out the last wish of Robert Bruce, pervades the castle in the emblem of a winged heart, found throughout the building.

The gardens, now being restored to the plan of 1738, add to the overall effect. The fascination of Drumlanrig as a centre of art, beauty and history is complemented by its role in the Queensberry Estate, a model of dynamic and enlightened land management.

CONTACT

A Fisher
Drumlanrig Castle
Thornhill
Dumfriesshire
DG3 4AQ

Tel: (01848) 330248

Fax: (01848) 600244

LOCATION

OS Ref. NX851 992

18m N of Dumfries,
3m NW of Thornhill
off A76.
16m from M74 at
Elvanfoot.
Approx. 1½ hrs
by road from Edinburgh,
Glasgow and Carlisle.

OPENING TIMES

SUMMER

Castle
3 May - 31 August
11am - 5pm.

Last entry to castle
4.15pm.

Castle closed Thur.

Gardens & Country Park
11am - 6pm throughout.

WINTER
By arrangement only.

ADMISSION

SUMMER

Adult	£4.00
Child	£2.00
OAP	£2.50
Family	£10.00

Groups
Adult	£2.50
Child	£2.00
OAP	£2.50

CONFERENCE/FUNCTION

ROOM	SIZE	MAX CAPACITY
Visitors' Centre	6m x 13m	50

i   Shop. No photography inside the castle. Restricted route in castle 11 - 13 July inclusive.

Welcome. Please enquire about facilities before visit.

Tearoom in castle. Snacks, lunches and teas during opening hours.

Available in the early season and by prior arrangement.

P   Adjacent to the castle.

Children's quiz and worksheets. Ranger-led activities, including woodlands and forestry. Adventure playground. Bird of prey centre.

CONTACT

Philip Massey
Director of Operations
Roxburghe Estates Office
Kelso
Roxburghshire
Scotland
TD5 7SF

Tel: (01573) 223333

Fax: (01573) 226056

LOCATION

OS Ref. NT711 347

From South A68, A698.

From North A68, A697/9
In Kelso follow signs.

Bus: Kelso Bus Station 1m.

Rail: Berwick 20m.

CONFERENCE/FUNCTION		
ROOM	SIZE	MAX CAPACITY
Dining Rm	18m x 7m	150
Ballroom	21m x 8m	150
Roxburghe Room	6m x 5m	25

FLOORS CASTLE
Kelso

FLOORS CASTLE, home of the Duke and Duchess of Roxburghe is situated in the heart of the Scottish Border Country. It is reputedly the largest inhabited castle in Scotland. Designed by William Adam, who was both masterbuilder and architect, for the first Duke of Roxburghe, building started in 1721.

It was the present Duke's great-great-grand-father James, the 6th Duke, who embellished the plain Adam features of the building. In about 1849 Playfair, letting his imagination and talent run riot, transformed the Castle, creating a multitude of spires and domes.

Externally the castle has not been altered since the 6th Duke's time, but internally, several of the rooms, including the dining room and ballroom, were remodelled at the turn of the century. These apartments now display the outstanding collection of French 17th and 18th century furniture, magnificent tapestries, Chinese and European porcelain and many other fine works of art. Many of the treasures in the castle today were collected by Duchess May, American wife of the 8th Duke.

The castle has been seen on cinema screens worldwide in the film *Greystoke*, as the home of Tarzan, the Earl of Greystoke.

Gardens

The extensive parkland and gardens overlooking the Tweed provide a variety of wooded walks. The walled garden contains splendid herbaceous borders and in the outer walled garden a summerhouse built for Queen Victoria's visit in 1867 can still be seen. An excellent children's playground and picnic area are very close to the castle.

ℹ Shop. Gala dinners, conferences, product launches, incentive groups, 4 x 4 driving, highland games and other promotional events. Extensive park, helicopter pad, fishing, clay pigeon and pheasant shooting. No photography inside the castle.

♿ Visitors may alight at the entrance. WC.

☕ Self-service, licensed restaurant, seating 125 opens 10am. Groups can book.

🚶 On request for up to 100. Tour time 1¼ hrs.

🅿 Unlimited for cars, 100 yds away, coach park 50 yds. Coaches can be driven to the entrance, waiting area close to restaurant exit. Lunch or tea for coach drivers.

👫 Welcome, guide provided. Playground facilities.

🐕 No dogs.

OPENING TIMES

SUMMER

Easter - September
daily: 10am - 4.30pm.

October
Sun & Wed: 10am - 4pm.

WINTER

November - March
Closed to the general public.

ADMISSION

SUMMER

Adult £4.50
OAP.........................£3.75
Child (5 - 15yrs) £2.50
Family £12.00

Groups
Adult £3.40
OAP.........................£3.25
Child (5 - 15yrs) £2.00

KELBURN CASTLE
& COUNTRY CENTRE
Largs

The historic home of the Boyle family, later Earls of Glasgow, Kelburn is situated on the picturesque north Ayrshire coast. It dates from the 13th century and is thought to be the oldest Castle in Scotland inhabited by the same family.

The original 1200 Norman Keep was extended in 1580 by a Tower House, and a William and Mary Mansion House was added in 1700 by David Boyle, created 1st Earl of Glasgow by Queen Anne in 1703 for his role in the Act of Union. The Victorian wing was built in 1879. Kelburn's essential charm is its informal family atmosphere, varied internal decor, and stunning location.

The grounds at Kelburn are quite lovely. Romantic Kelburn Glen has winding wood-land trails, waterfalls and deep gorges. The Plaisance, a formal walled garden, is dominated by two 1,000 year old yew trees, and a children's garden is planted in the form of the Saltire. A Robert Adam monument, 18th century sundial and ice house, are among Kelburn's featured historical attractions. Kelburn's newest attraction, The Secret Forest, has unusual follies such as The Maze of The Green Man, a Chinese Pagoda, Gingerbread House, Grotto, Crocodile Swamp and Chinese Garden.

Within the Country Centre there is The Kelburn Story Cartoon Exhibition, a family museum, horse riding, adventure play areas, commando assault course, soft play room, pets' corner, nature centre, activity workshop, information centre, ranger service and picnic areas. Birds of prey displays May - Aug. Events every weekend July, August and September.

❖

CONTACT

Earl of Glasgow
Kelburn Castle &
Country Centre
South Offices
Fairlie, Nr Largs,
Ayrshire KA29 0BE

Tel: Country Centre:
(01475) 568685

Castle: (01475) 568204

Fax: Country Centre:
(01475) 568121

Castle: (01475) 568328

LOCATION

OS Ref. NS210 580

M8 Edinburgh to Glasgow,
M8 Glasgow to Greenock,
A78 to Largs, A78 main
coastal trunk road
Off A78 coast road 2m
S of Largs.

Rail: Largs station 2m.

Bus: A78 main bus
route to Ayr, stop
adjacent to property.

Taxis: A2B taxis
(01475) 673976.

CONFERENCE/FUNCTION		
ROOM	SIZE	MAX CAPACITY
Drawing Rm	33' x 24'	60
Dining Rm		60

i Shop. Corporate events, clay pigeon shoots, exhibitions, business meetings, conferences, fashion shows, filming, product launches, nature activities and barbeques. Helicopter landing pad.

✗ Full catering facilities for functions / conferences.

♿ Visitors may alight at the entrance. WC. Some stairs.

☕ Licensed restaurant and café. Groups can book, special rates for groups.

Max. 25, no additional cost, tour time 45 mins. Lectures on castle, grounds and history if booked. Ranger tour of grounds.

P Ample. Coach passengers can alight at the forecourt, coach park 5 - 10 mins walk.

Welcome. Teachers free, ratio of 1:10. Ranger service for guided walks and nature activities. Worksheets, pets corner, pony rides/treks, adventure play areas.

A Available.

OPENING TIMES

SUMMER
Castle
July & August
Tours: 1.45pm, 3pm &
4.15pm. (Except when
there are afternoon
functions).

Tours can be arranged at
other times of the year.

Country Centre
& Gardens
Easter - end October
daily: 10am - 6pm.

WINTER
Castle
By special
arrangement only.

Country Centre
End October - Easter
11am - 5pm
Grounds only.

ADMISSION

SUMMER
Castle only
  Per person £1.50
  Student...................£1.20

(These prices do not include
entry fee to Centre)

Country Centre
  Adult £4.00
  Child* £2.50
  Conc.....................£2.50
Groups (min 12)
  Adult £3.00
  Child* £1.75
  Conc.....................£1.75

WINTER
Castle only
As Summer rates.

Country Centre
  Adult £1.75
  Child* £1.00

* Accompanied children
2 - school age.

MANDERSTON
Duns

MANDERSTON, together with its magnificent stables, stunning marble dairy and 56 acres of immaculate garden, forms an ensemble which must be unique in Britain today.

The house was completely rebuilt between 1903 and 1905, with no expense spared.

Visitors are able to see not only the sumptuous State Rooms and bedrooms, decorated in the Adam manner, but also all the original domestic offices, in a truly 'upstairs downstairs' atmosphere. Manderston boasts a unique and recently restored silver staircase.

There is a special museum with a nostalgic display of valuable tins made by Huntley and Palmers from 1868 to the present day. *Winner of the AA / NPI Bronze Award UK 1994.*

GARDENS

Outside, the magnificence continues and the combination of formal gardens and picturesque landscapes is a major attraction: unique amongst Scottish houses.

The stables, still in use, have been described by *Horse and Hound* as "probably the finest in all the wide world."

CONTACT

The Lord or Lady Palmer
Manderston
Duns
Berwickshire
Scotland
TD11 3PP

Tel: (01361) 883450
(01361) 882636

Fax: (01361) 882010

www: http://www.twisel.co.uk/borders/shomes/manderston.html

LOCATION

OS Ref. NT810 544

From Edinburgh 47m, 1hr. 1¹/₂ m E of Duns on A6105.

Bus: 400 yds.

Rail: Berwick Station 12m.

Taxi: Chirnside 818216.

Airport: Edinburgh or Newcastle both 60m or 80 mins.

i Shop. Fashion shows, air displays, archery, clay pigeon shooting, equestrian events, garden parties, shows, rallies, filming, product launches and marathons. Two airstrips for light aircraft, approx 5m, grand piano, billiard table, fox hunting, pheasant shoots, sea angling, salmon fishing, stabling, cricket pitch, tennis court, lake. Nearby: 9-hole golf course, indoor swimming pool, squash court. No photography in house.

✕ Available. Buffets, lunches and dinners. Wedding receptions.

♿ Special parking available outside the House.

☕ Tearoom (open as house) with waitress service. Can be booked in advance, menus on request.

🚶 Included in price. Available in French. Guides in rooms. If requested, the owner may meet groups. Tour time 1¹/₄ hrs.

P 400 cars 125yds from house, 30 coaches 5yds from house. Appreciated if group fees are paid by one person.

👫 Welcome. Guide can be provided. Biscuit Tin Museum of particular interest.

🐕 Grounds only, on leads.

A 5 twin, 4 double and 1 single.

CONFERENCE/FUNCTION

ROOM	SIZE	MAX CAPACITY
Dining Rm	22'x 35'	100
Ballroom	34'x 21'	150
Hall	22'x 38'	130
Drawing Rm	35'x 21'	150

OPENING TIMES

SUMMER

Mid May - September
Thur & Sun
2 - 5.30pm.

BH Mon, late May
& August
2 - 5.30pm.

Group visits at other times by arrangement.

WINTER

September - May
Group visits welcome by arrangement.

ADMISSION

House & Grounds

Adult £5.00
Child £1.00
Groups (min 20 on open days)
Per person £3.00
School child...........£1.50
(min Student group £45.00)

Grounds only

Including Stables &
Marble Dairy
Adult £2.50
Child £0.50
Groups (min 20)
Per person £2.00

On days when the house is closed to the public, parties viewing by appointment will have personally conducted tours. The Gift Shop will be open. On these occasions reduced party rates (except for school children) will not apply. Group visits other than open days are £5pp (min £100). Cream teas on open days only.

TRAQUAIR
Innerleithen

TRAQUAIR, situated amidst beautiful scenery and close by the River Tweed, is the oldest inhabited house in Scotland – visited by twenty-seven kings. Originally a Royal Hunting Lodge, it was owned by the Scottish Crown until 1478 when it passed to a branch of the Royal Stuart family whose descendants still live in the House today.

From a single tower block the building grew, reflecting the growth and importance of the Stuarts of Traquair and no exterior alterations were made after the end of the 17th century. At the end of the tree-lined avenue leading to the House are the famous Bear Gates closed since 1745 when the last person to pass through them was Bonnie Prince Charlie (not to be opened again until the restoration of the Stuarts).

Nearly ten centuries of Scottish political and domestic life can be traced from the collection of treasures in the House. It is particularly rich in associations with the Catholic Church in Scotland, Mary Queen of Scots and the Jacobite Risings.

GARDEN

70 acres of grounds with peacocks, ducks and other wildlife. In spring there is a profusion of daffodils followed by rhododendrons, wild flowers and herbaceous plants. A maze in beech/leylandii cyprus is behind the House.

CONTACT

Ms C Maxwell Stuart
Traquair House
Innerleithen
Peeblesshire
EH44 6PW

Tel: (01896) 830323

Fax: (01896) 830639

e-mail:
Traquair.house@scotborders.co.uk

LOCATION

OS Ref. NY330 354

From Edinburgh 1 hr,
Glasgow $1^1/2$ hrs,
Carlisle $1^1/2$ hrs,
Newcastle $2^1/2$ hrs.
On B709 near
junction with A72.

Rail: Edinburgh
Waverley 30m.

Bus: Hourly bus service
from Edinburgh to
Innerleithen.
Enquiries: Lowland
Omnibuses (0131) 558 1616.

Taxi: Leithen Valley Taxis
(01896) 830486

CONFERENCE/FUNCTION		
ROOM	SIZE	MAX CAPACITY
Dining Rm	33' x 18'	30
Drawing Room	27' x 24'	60

i Shop. Meetings and dinners, product launches, filming, archery, clay-pigeon shooting, theatre, son et lumière. 18th century fully operational Brewhouse, ale tasting every Fri, 3 - 4pm. 17th century harpsichord in drawing room, croquet (mallets can be hired). Lectures provided on the property, contents, history and grounds. No photography in House. Guide book translations in French, Spanish, German, Dutch, Swedish, Japanese and Italian.

X Marquee (lined and floored) available for wedding receptions, etc., in the gardens or courtyard. Lunches and dinners in dining room from £30pp by special arrangement.

(wheelchair) Visitors may alight at entrance. WCs.

(tearoom) Licensed self-service 1745 Cottage Tearoom. On fine days lunches and teas can be taken outdoors. Groups of up to 45 can be served in the Bear Cottage.

(walking) Tours only outside opening hours £4.25pp (£80 min). Introductory talks can be given to groups. Out of hours visits with meals/refreshments by prior arrangement.

P Ample, 85 yds from House. Coaches preferably booked in advance. Drivers please apply for vouchers on arrival.

(dog) Dogs on leads in grounds.

A Traquair offers 2 fourposter suites with bathroom on a bed and breakfast basis.

OPENING TIMES

SUMMER
29 March - 30 September
daily: 12.30 - 5.30pm.

June, July & August
10.30am - 5.30pm
Last admission 5pm.

October: Fri - Sun
2 - 5pm.

Restaurant: 12 - 5.30pm
June, July & August
from 11am.

WINTER
1 November - Easter
open by arrangement.

ADMISSION

SUMMER
House & Garden
Adult £4.00
Child* £2.00
Groups**
Adult £3.20
Child* £1.60

Garden only
Adult £1.50
Child* £1.00

* Under 15 years.
** Minimum payment £60 when House open £80 when closed.

WINTER
£6.00 per person.

Includes glass of wine/whisky/Traquair Ale and shortbread.
Minimum charge £100.

SPECIAL EVENTS

- **MAR 30:**
Easter Egg Extravaganza

- **MAY 24/25:**
Scottish Beer Festival

- **SEPT 13/14:**
Traquair Needlework Weekend

ABBOTSFORD HOUSE 🏛

MELROSE, ROXBURGHSHIRE TD6 9BQ

Owner: Mrs P Maxwell-Scott OBE   *Contact:* Mrs P Maxwell-Scott OBE

Tel: 01896 752043 **Fax:** 01896 752916

Sir Walter Scott purchased the Cartley Hall farmhouse on the banks of the Tweed in 1812. Together with his family and servants he moved into the farm which he renamed Abbotsford. Scott had the old house demolished in 1822 and replaced it with the main block of Abbotsford as it is today. Scott was a passionate collector of historic relics including an impressive collection of armour and weapons and over 9,000 rare volumes in his library.

Location: OS Ref. NT508 343. 35m S of Edinburgh. Melrose 3m, Galashiels 2m.

Opening Times: 17 Mar - 31 Oct: Mon - Sat, 10am - 5pm, Sun, 2 - 5 pm. Other dates by arrangement.

Admission: Adult £3.40, Child / Student £1.70. Groups: Adult £2.35, Child £1.20.

ⓘ Shop.   ♿ House suitable. WC.   ☕ Tearoom.   🐕 Guide dogs only.

ARBIGLAND GARDENS 🏛

KIRKBEAN, DUMFRIES & GALLOWAY DG2 8BQ

Owner: Capt & Mrs Beauchamp Blackett *Contact:* Capt & Mrs Beauchamp Blackett

Tel: 01387 880283

Formal woodland and water gardens which have evolved through three centuries. The ideal family outing garden as the gardens run down to a sheltered sandy bay where the younger members (and dogs) can let off steam. 400 yards from the John Paul Jones Birthplace Museum, his father created the gardens circa 1750.

Location: OS Ref. NX990 574. 15m S of Dumfries off A710 'Solway Coast Road'.

Opening Times: 1 May - 30 Sept: Tue - Sun plus BH Mon 2 - 6pm. House open Fri 23 May - Sun 1 Jun and by appointment.

Admission: Adult £2, OAP £1.50, Child 50p, Toddlers Free.

ⓘ Shop. ♿ Grounds suitable. WC. ☕ Tearoom. 🐕 In grounds, on leads.

SPECIAL EVENTS

JUL 4 – 6: Various events to mark the 250th birthday of John Paul Jones.

AYTON CASTLE 🏛

AYTON, EYEMOUTH, BERWICKSHIRE TD14 5RD

Owner: D I Liddell-Grainger of Ayton   *Contact:* The Curator

Tel: 018907 81212 or 018907 81550

Built in 1846 by the Mitchell-Innes family and designed by the architect James Gillespie Graham. Over the last ten years it has been fully restored and is now a family home. It is a unique restoration project and the quality of the original and restored workmanship is outstanding. The castle stands on an escarpment surrounded by mature woodlands containing many interesting trees and has been a film-making venue due to this magnificent setting.

Location: OS Ref. NT920 610. 7m N of Berwick-on-Tweed on Route A1.

Opening Times: 4 May - 14 Sept: Sun, 2 - 5 pm or by appointment.

Admission: Adult £2, Child under 5 Free.

BACHELORS' CLUB ♟   **Tel:** 01292 541940

Sandgate Street, Tarbolton KA5 5RB

Owner: The National Trust for Scotland   **Contact:** David Rodger

17th century thatched house in which poet Robert Burns and friends formed a debating society in 1780. Burns' mementos and relics, period furnishings.

Location: OS Ref. NS430 270. In Tarbolton, B744, 7½ m NE of Ayr, off B743.

Opening Times: Good Fri - 30 Sept: daily 11.30 - 5pm. Weekends in Oct: 11.30 - 5pm. Last admission 4.30pm.

Admission: Adult £1.80, Conc. £1.20, Family £4.80. Groups: Adult £1.50, School £1.

♿ Ground floor suitable.   🐕 No dogs.

BLAIRQUHAN CASTLE 🏛   **See page 45 for full page entry.**

BOWHILL 🏛   **See page 46 for full page entry.**

Traquair – the library, Peebleshire.

BRODICK CASTLE & COUNTRY PARK ☙

Douglas Macgregor

ISLE OF ARRAN KA27 8HY

Owner: *The National Trust for Scotland*   ***Contact:*** *Veronica Woodman*

Tel: 01770 302202

This is a castle you will never forget ! The tall, stately building beckons you with the glow of its warm red sandstone. The setting is staggering, fronted by the sea, bedecked with gardens and overlooked by the majestic mountain of Goatfell. The castle was built on the site of a Viking fortress and dates from the 13th century. The contents are magnificent and include superb silver, porcelain, paintings and sporting trophies. The woodland garden ranks as one of Europe's finest.

Location: OS Ref. NS010 360. Isle of Arran. Ferries from Ardrossan & Claonaig and Kintyre. Ferry enquiries: 01475 650100

Opening Times: Castle: Good Fri - 31 Oct: daily 11.30am - 5pm. Last admission 4.30pm. Reception Centre and shop (dates as castle) 10am - 5pm; restaurant 11am - 5pm. Garden & Country Park: All year, daily 9.30am - sunset. Goatfell open all year.

Admission: Castle: Adult £4.50, Child £3. Groups: Adult £3.60, School £1, Family £12. Garden & Country Park: Adult £2.30, Child £1.50, Family £6.10. Groups: Adult £1.80, School £1. .

ⓘ Shop. ♿ Suitable. WC. ☕ Licensed restaurant. 🐕 In grounds, on leads.

BROUGHTON HOUSE & GARDEN ☙

J. Wilkie

HIGH STREET, KIRKCUDBRIGHT DG6 4JX

Owner: *The National Trust for Scotland (in process of transfer)* ***Contact:*** *Frances Scott*

Tel: 01557 330437

This fascinating 18th century house in the pleasant coastal town of Kirkcudbright was the home and studio from 1901 - 1933 of the artist E A Hornel, one of the 'Glasgow Boys'. It contains a superb collection of his work, along with paintings by other contemporary artists, and an extensive library of rare Scottish books, including valuable editions of Burns's works.

Location: OS Ref. NX684 509. Off A711 / A755, in Kirkcudbright, at 12 High St.

Opening Times: House & Garden: 28 Mar - 31 Oct, daily, 1 - 5.30pm. Last admission 4.45pm.

Admission: Adult £2.30, Child £1.50, Family £6.10. Groups: Adult £1.80, School £1. Family £6.10.

♿ Not suitable. 🚶 By arrangement. Ⓟ Limited. 🐕 No dogs.

BURNS COTTAGE **Tel:** 01292 441215

Alloway, Ayrshire KA7 4PY **Contact:** J Manson

Thatched cottage, birthplace of Robert Burns in 1759. Now a museum.

Location: OS Ref. NS335 190. 2m SW of Ayr.

Opening Times: Apr - May: Mon - Sat, 10am - 5pm. Sun 1 - 5pm. Jun - Aug: Mon - Sat, 10am - 5pm. Sun 1 - 5pm. Nov - Mar: 9am - 4pm. Sun 10am - 6pm. Sept - Oct: 10am - 4pm. Closed Sun.

Admission: Adult £2.50, Child £1.25, OAP £1.85, Family £6. Admission charge includes entry to Burns' Monument and Gardens.

CAERLAVEROCK CASTLE   **Tel:** 01387 770244

Dumfries

Owner: Historic Scotland **Contact:** The Custodian

Caerlaverock (Lark's Nest) is everyone's idea of a medieval fortress. Its most remarkable features are the twin-towered gatehouse and the Nithsdale Lodging, a splendid Renaissance Range dating from 1638. The scene of two famous sieges. This moated castle has a children's adventure park and model siege engine in its grounds.

Location: OS Ref. NY026 656. 8m SE of Dumfries on the B725. 3m SE of Glencaple.

Opening Times: 1 Apr - 30 Sept: Mon - Sat 9.30am - 6.30pm, Sun 2 - 6.30pm. Last ticket 6pm. 1 Oct - 31 Mar: Mon - Sat, 9.30am - 4.30pm, Sun 2 - 4.30pm. Last ticket 4pm.

Admission: Adult £2.30, Child £1, Conc. £1.50.

CARDONESS CASTLE 🏰 **Tel:** 01557 814427

Gatehouse of Fleet

Owner: Historic Scotland **Contact:** The Custodian

Well preserved ruin of a four storey tower house of 15th century standing on a rocky platform above the Water of Fleet. Ancient home of the McCullochs. Very fine fireplaces.

Location: OS Ref. NX591 553. 1m SW of Gatehouse of Fleet, beside the A75.

Opening Times: 1 Apr - 30 Sept: Mon - Sat 9.30am - 6.30pm, Sun 2 - 6.30pm. Last ticket 6pm. 1 Oct - 31 Mar: Sat 9.30am - 4.30pm, Sun 2 - 4.30pm. Last ticket 4pm.

Admission: Adult £1.50, Child 75p, Conc. £1.

CARLYLE'S BIRTHPLACE ☙ **Tel:** 01576 300666

Ecclefechan, Dumfriesshire

Owner: The National Trust for Scotland **Contact:** The Manager

Thomas Carlyle was born here in The Arched House in 1795, the year before Burns died. Carlyle was a brilliant essayist, historian, social reformer, visionary and literary giant. When he was 14 he walked the 84 miles to Edinburgh University - taking three days. Upstairs is the bedroom in which Carlyle was born. There is also a little museum with a notable collection of photographs, manuscripts and other documents.

Location: OS Ref. NY193 745. Off M74, 6m SE of Lockerbie. 1m Ecclefechan village.

Opening Times: 1 May - 30 Sept: Fri - Mon 1.30 - 5.30pm. Last admission 5pm.

Admission: Adult £1.80, Child £1.20. Groups: Adult £1.50, School £1. Family £4.80.

♿ Not suitable. 🚶 By arrangement. Ⓟ Limited. 🐕 No dogs.

CROSSRAGUEL ABBEY 🏰 **Tel:** 01655 883113

Maybole, Strathclyde

Owner: Historic Scotland **Contact:** The Custodian

Founded in the early 13th century by the Earl of Carrick. Remarkably complete remains include church, cloister, chapter house and much of the domestic premises.

Location: OS Ref. NS275 083. 2m S of Maybole on the A77.

Opening Times: 1 Apr - 30 Sept: Mon - Sat 9.30am - 6.30pm. Sun 2 - 6.30pm. Last ticket 6pm. Closed Thur pm & Fri in winter.

Admission: Adult £1.50, Child 75p, Conc. £1.

Kelburn Castle, Ayrshire.

CULZEAN CASTLE & COUNTRY PARK

MAYBOLE KA19 8LE

Owner: *The National Trust for Scotland*   **Contact:** *Jonathan Cardale*

Tel: 01655 760274

Robert Adam's 18th century masterpiece, a real 'castle in the air', is perched on a cliff high above the crashing waves of the Firth of Clyde. Arrow slits and mock battlements give medieval touches to the sturdy exterior, and on the seaward-side front is the imposing drum tower. The interior is the epitome of disciplined elegance, crowned by the spectacular oval staircase ascending through ornamental pillars and ironwork balustrading. Adam also designed many interior fittings. The exterior grounds encompass Scotland's first country park.

Location: OS Ref. NS240 100. 12m SW of Ayr, on A719, 4m W of Maybole.

Opening Times: Castle, Visitor Centre, licensed restaurant and shops: 28 Mar - 31 Oct: daily 10.30am - 5.30pm. Last admission 5pm. Other times by appointment. Country Park: All year, daily 9.30am - sunset.

Admission: Castle: Adult £4, Child £2.70, Family £10.70. Country Park only: Adult £3, Child £2, Family £8, School coach £20. Castle & Park: Adult £6, Child £4, Family £16. Groups: Adult £4.80.

 Shop.   Suitable. WC.   Licensed restaurant.   In grounds, on leads.

DUNS CASTLE

DUNS, BERWICKSHIRE TD11 3NW

Owner: *Alexander Hay of Duns*   **Contact:** *Mrs Aline Hay*

Tel: 01361 883211   **Fax:** 01361 882015

This historical 1320 peel tower has been home to the Hay family since 1696, and the current owners Alexander and Aline Hay offer it as a welcoming venue for individuals, groups and corporate guests to enjoy. They have renovated it to produce the highest standards of comfort while retaining all the character of its rich period interiors. Wonderful lakeside and parkland setting.

Location: OS Ref. NT777 544. 10m off A4. Rail: Berwick station 16m. Airports: Newcastle & Edinburgh, 1 hr.

Opening Times: Not open to the public except by arrangement and for individuals, groups and companies for day or residential stays. Available all year.

Admission: Rates for private and corporate visits, wedding receptions, filming by arrangement.

A   4 x four-poster, 3 x double, 3 x twin (all with bathrooms), 2 single.

DAWYCK BOTANIC GARDEN   **Tel:** 01721 760254 **Fax:** 01721 760214

Stobo, Peeblesshire EH45 9JU   **Contact:** The Curator

Renowned historic arboretum. Follow the landscaped walks to discover Dawyck's secrets. Amongst mature specimen trees - some over 40 metres tall - are a variety of flowering trees, shrubs and herbaceous plants. Explore the world's first Cryptogamic Sanctuary and Reserve for 'non-flowering' plants.

Location: NT168 352. 8m SW of Peebles on B712.

Opening Times: 15 Mar - 22 Oct: daily, 10am - 6pm.

Admission: Adult £2, Child 50p, Family £4.50, Conc. £1.50, Group discounts available.

 Shop & plant centre.   Grounds suitable. WC.   Guide dogs only.

DRUMLANRIG CASTLE   See page 47 for full page entry.

DRYBURGH ABBEY   **Tel:** 01835 822381

St Boswells, Melrose

Owner: Historic Scotland   **Contact:** The Custodian

The ruins of Dryburgh Abbey are remarkably complete. The burial place of Sir Walter Scott and Field Marshal Earl Haig. Perhaps the most beautiful of all the Border abbeys.

Location: OS Ref. NT591 317. 5m SE of Melrose off B6356. 1^1/2 m N of St Boswells.

Opening Times: 1 Apr - 30 Sept: Mon - Sat 9.30am - 6.30pm, Sun 2 - 6.30pm. Last ticket 6pm. 1 Oct - 31 Mar: Mon - Sat 9.30am - 4.30pm, Sun, 2 - 4.30pm, last ticket 4pm.

Admission: Adult £2.30, Child £1, Conc. £1.50.

DUNDRENNAN ABBEY   **Tel:** 01557 500262

Kirkcudbright

Owner: Historic Scotland   **Contact:** The Custodian

Mary Queen of Scots spent her last night on Scottish soil in this 12th century Cistercian Abbey founded by David I. The Abbey stands in a small and secluded valley.

Location: OS Ref. NX749 475. 6^1/2 m SE of Kirkcudbright on the A711.

Opening Times: 1 Apr - 30 Sept: Mon - Wed & Sat, 9.30am - 6.30pm, Thur 9.30am - 12 pm, Fri closed, Sun 2 - 6.30pm. Last ticket 6pm.

Admission: Adult £1.50, Child 75p, Conc. £1.

FLOORS CASTLE   See page 48 for full page entry.

GALLOWAY HOUSE GARDENS   **Tel:** 01988 600680

Garlieston, Newton Stewart, Wigtownshire DG8 8HF

Owner: Galloway House Gardens Trust   **Contact:** D Marshall

Location: OS Ref. NX478 453. 15m S of Newton Stewart on B7004.

Opening Times: 1 Mar - 31 Oct: 9am - 5pm.

Admission: Adult £1, Child 50p, Family £2.50, Conc. 50p.

GLENLUCE ABBEY   **Tel:** 01581 300541

Glenluce

Owner: Historic Scotland   **Contact:** Historic Scotland

A Cistercian Abbey founded in 1190. Remains include a handsome 16th century Chapter House.

Location: OS Ref. NX185 587. 2m NW of Glenluce village off the A75.

Opening Times: 1 Apr - 30 Sept: Mon - Sat 9.30am - 6.30pm, Sun 2 - 6.30pm. Last ticket 6pm. 1 Oct - 31 Mar: Sat 9.30am - 4.30pm, Sun 2 - 4.30pm. Last ticket 4pm.

Admission: Adult £1.50, Child 75p, Conc. £1.

HERMITAGE CASTLE   **Tel:** 013873 762225

Liddesdale, Newcastleton

Owner: Historic Scotland   **Contact:** The Custodian

Eerie fortress at the heart of the bloodiest events in the history of the Borders. Mary Queen of Scots made her famous ride here to visit her future husband.

Location: OS Ref. NY497 961. In Liddesdale 5^1/2 m NE of Newcastleton, B6399.

Opening Times: 1 Apr - 30 Sept: Mon - Sat 9.30am - 6.30pm, Sun 2 - 6.30pm. Last ticket 6pm. Winter - Closed Mon - Fri.

Admission: Adult £1.50, Child 75p, Conc. £1.

THE HIRSEL GARDENS

Tel: 01890 882834 **Fax:** 01890 882834

Coldstream, Berwickshire TD12 4LP   **Contact:** Hirsel Estate Office

Wonderful spring flowers and rhododendrons. Homestead museum and crafts centre.

Location: OS Ref. NT838 393. Immediately W of Coldstream off A697.

Opening Times: Grounds - all year: daily during daylight hours. Museum and craft shop open 10am - 5pm weekdays, 12 - 5pm weekends.

Admission: Parking charge only.

 Shop.

KELBURN CASTLE

See page 49 for full page entry.

LOGAN BOTANIC GARDEN

Tel: 01776 860231 **Fax:** 01776 860333

Port Logan, Stranraer, Wigtownshire DG9 9ND

Owner: Royal Botanic Garden Edinburgh   **Contact:** The Curator

Scotland's most exotic garden. Take a trip to the south west of Scotland and experience the southern hemisphere! The exceptionally mild climate allows a colourful array of tender exotics to thrive out of doors - tree ferns, cabbage palms, unusual shrubs, climbers and tender perennials.

Location: OS Ref. NX097 430. 14m S of Stranraer on B7065.

Opening Times: 15 Mar - 31 Oct: daily, 10am - 6pm.

Admission: Adult £2, Child 50p, Family £4.50, Conc. £1.50. Group discount available.

i Shop.   Licensed salad bar.   By arrangement.   Guide dogs only.

MACLELLAN'S CASTLE

Tel: 01557 331856

Kirkcudbright

Owner: Historic Scotland   **Contact:** The Custodian

A handsome castellated mansion, built in 1577 using stone from an adjoining ruined monastery by the then Provost. Elaborately planned with fine architectural details, it has been a ruin since 1752.

Location: OS Ref. NX683 511. Centre of Kirkcudbright on the A711.

Opening Times: 1 Apr - 30 Sept: Mon - Sat, 9.30am - 6.30pm, Sun 2 - 6.30pm. Last ticket 6pm.

Admission: Adult £1, Child 50p, Conc. 50p.

MANDERSTON

See page 50 for full page entry.

MAXWELTON HOUSE

Tel: 01848 200385

Moniaive, Thornhill, Dumfries & Galloway DG3 4DX

Owner: Maxwelton House Trust   **Contact:** Roderick Stenhouse

Glencairn Castle now Maxwelton House dates back to 1370, the home of the Earls of Glencairn. Stephen Laurie bought Glencairn Castle in 1611 and changed the name to Maxwelton. Annie Laurie was born here in 1682. The Stenhouse family purchased Maxwelton from the Laurie family in 1968 and carried out one of the largest restorations to a private house within Scotland. The restoration took three years and the continuing labour of no less than 65 men. It was completed in 1972. House, museum, Chapel.

Location: OS Ref. NX822 898. Entrances on B729 near Wallaceton or A702 near Penpont. 13m NW of Dumfries.

Opening Times: Last Sun in May - end Sept: Sun - Fri (closed Sat) 11am - 5pm. Apr - 24 May open for groups only. Last admission ½ hr before closing.

Admission: Adult £3.50, Child (up to 16yrs) £2, Conc. £3. Groups: £3pp. Garden only: £2.

i Shop.   Tearoom.   Compulsory.   *P* Free parking.   In grounds, on leads.

Manderston – boss on dairy ceiling, Berwickshire.

MELLERSTAIN HOUSE

MELLERSTAIN, GORDON, BERWICKSHIRE TD3 6LG

Owner: *The Earl of Haddington*   **Contact:** *Mrs. F. Turnbull*

Tel: 01573 410225

One of Scotland's great Georgian houses and a unique example of the work of the Adam family; the two wings built in 1725 by William Adam, the large central block by his son, Robert 1770-78. Rooms contain fine plasterwork, colourful ceilings and marble fireplaces. The library is considered to be Robert Adam's finest creation. Many fine paintings and period furniture.

Location: OS Ref. NT648 392. From Edinburgh A68 to Earlston, turn left 5m, signed.

Opening Times: Easter weekend (Fri - Mon), 1 May - 30 Sept, daily except Sat, 12.30 - 5pm. Groups at other times by appointment.

Admission: Adult £4, Conc. £3, Child £1.50. Groups (min. 20) £3. Grounds only: £1.50.

i Shop.   Ground floor & grounds suitable.   Tearoom.   In grounds.

MELROSE ABBEY

Tel: 01896 822562

Melrose

Owner: Historic Scotland   **Contact:** The Custodian

Its 14th to 16th century remains retain a unique elegance. Said to be the burial place of Robert the Bruce's heart. Founded around 1136 as a Cistercian Abbey by David I.

Location: OS Ref. NT549 342. In Melrose off the A7 or A68.

Opening Times: 1 Apr - 30 Sept: Mon - Sat 9.30am - 6.30pm, Sun 2 - 6.30pm. Last ticket 6pm. 1 Oct - 31 Mar: Mon - Sat, 9.30am - 4.30pm, Sun 2 - 4.30pm. Last ticket 4pm.

Admission: Adult £2.80, Conc. £1.80, Child £1. Includes audio tour.

MERTOUN GARDENS

Tel: 01835 823236 **Fax:** 01835 822474

St Boswells, Melrose, Roxburgh TD6 0EA

Owner: The Duke of Sutherland   **Contact:** Miss Miller

26 acres of beautiful grounds. Walled garden and well preserved circular dovecote.

Location: OS Ref. NT617 318. Entrance off B6404 2m NE of St Boswells.

Opening Times: Apr - Sept: weekends only and BH Mon only, 9am - 6pm. Last admission 5.30pm.

Admission: Adult £1, Child 50p. Groups by arrangement: Adult 90p, Child 45p.

By arrangement.   No dogs.

NEIDPATH CASTLE

Tel/Fax: 01721 720333

Peebles, Scottish Borders EH45 8NW

Owner: Lady Elizabeth Benson   **Contact:** The Custodian

Authentic 14th century castle converted to tower house (17th century) home of Fraser, Hay and Douglas families. Pit prison, Laigh Hall with displays, Great Hall with 'Life of Mary Stuart' in Batik. Wonderful setting in wooded gorge of River Tweed.

Location: OS Ref. NT237 405. In Tweeddale 1m W of Peebles on A72.

Opening Times: Thur before Easter - 30 Sept: Mon - Sat, 11am - 5pm, Sun 1 - 5pm. Group bookings in Oct.

Admission: Adult £2, Child £1, Conc. £1.50, Family (2+3) £5.50. 10% discount for groups of 20+ .

i Shop.   Ground floor & grounds suitable.   In grounds, on leads.

NEW ABBEY CORN MILL

Tel: 01387 785260

New Abbey Village

Owner: Historic Scotland   **Contact:** The Custodian

This carefully renovated 18th century water-powered oatmeal mill is in full working order and regular demonstrations are given for visitors in the summer.

Location: OS Ref. NX962 663. 8m S of Dumfries on the A710. Close to Sweetheart Abbey.

Opening Times: 1 Apr - 30 Sept: Mon - Sat 9.30am - 6.30pm, Sun 2 - 6.30pm. Last ticket 6pm. 1 Oct - 31 Mar: Mon - Wed & Sat 9.30am - 4.30pm, Thur 9.30am - 12 noon, Fri closed, Sun 2 - 4.30pm. Last ticket 4pm.

Admission: Adult £2.30, Conc. £1.50, Child £1. Joint entry ticket with Sweetheart Abbey: Adult £2.80, Conc. £1.75, Child £1.25.

OLD GALA HOUSE

Tel: 01750 20096

Scot Crescent, Galashiels TD1 3JS

Owner: Mr Ian Brown   **Contact:** Mr Ian Brown

Dating from 1583 the former house of the Laird of Gala includes displays on the history of the house and its inhabitants and the early growth of Galashiels. Particularly memorable is the painted ceiling dated 1635.

Location: OS Ref. NT492 357. S of town centre, signed from A7.

Opening Times: Late Mar - early Nov: Mon - Sat 10am - 4pm, Sun 2 - 4pm (as at time of publication).

PAXTON HOUSE

BERWICK-UPON-TWEED TD15 1SZ

Owner: The Paxton Trust   *Contact: Martin Purslow*

Tel: 01289 386291   **Fax:** 01289 386660

Built in 1756 by John and James Adam, the house boasts the pre-eminent collection of Chippendale furniture on view in Scotland, the largest picture gallery in a Scottish country house, designed by Robert Reid in 1818, which now functions as an outstation for the National Galleries of Scotland, and a fine collection of Regency furniture by Trotter of Edinburgh. Other features include over 80 acres of woodland, parkland, gardens and riverside walks to explore, temporary exhibitions, highland cattle and croquet. Function suite for hire.

Location: OS Ref. NT931 520. 3m off the A1 Berwick-upon-Tweed on B6461.

Opening Times: 5 Apr - 31 Oct: Grounds: 10am - Sunset. House: 11am - 5pm. Last house tour 4.15pm. Open to groups/ schools all year by appointment.

Admission: Adult £4, Child £2. Grounds only: Adult £1.75, Child £1.

i Shop. Adventure playground.   Tearoom.

PRIORWOOD GARDEN & DRIED FLOWER SHOP

Melrose TD6 9PX

Tel: 01896 822493

Owner: The National Trust for Scotland   **Contact:** Mrs Cathy Ross

Overlooked by the Abbey's 15th century ruins is this unique garden, where most of the plants are suitable for drying. With the aid of volunteers, Priorwood Garden markets a wide variety of dried flower arrangements through its own dried flower shop.

Location: OS Ref. NT549 341. In the Border town of Melrose, beside the Abbey.

Opening Times: 28 Mar - 30 Sept: Mon - Sat 10am - 5.30pm, Sun 1.30 - 5.30pm. 1 Oct - 24 Dec: Mon - Sat 10am - 4pm, Sun 1.30 - 4pm.

Admission: Honesty box £1.

i Shop.   Grounds suitable. WC.   **P** No parking.   Guide dogs only.

ROBERT SMAIL'S PRINTING WORKS

HIGH STREET, INNERLEITHEN, PEEBLESSHIRE EH44 6HA

Owner: The National Trust for Scotland   *Contact: Edward Nicol*

Tel: 01896 830206

A printing time-capsule featuring a completely restored Victorian printing works. Visitors can experience the almost forgotten craft of hand typesetting. They will discover the secrets of the printing works from the archive-based posters and see the fully restored machines in action. The buildings also contain the Victorian office with its acid-etched windows, reconstructed waterwheel and many historic items which provide an insight into the history of the Border town of Innerleithen.

Location: OS Ref. NT333 366. In High Street, Innerleithen, 30m S of Edinburgh.

Opening Times: Good Fri - Easter Mon & 1 May - 30 Sept: Mon - Sat, 10am - 1pm & 2 - 5pm, Sun 2 - 5pm. Weekends in Oct: Sat: 10am - 1pm & 2 - 5pm, Sun 2 - 5pm. Last admission 45 mins before closing morning or afternoon).

Admission: Adult £2.30, Child £1.50, Family £6.10. Groups: Adult £1.80, School £1.

i Shop.   Ground floor suitable.   **P** No parking.   No dogs.

SMAILHOLM TOWER

Tel: 01573 460365

Smailholm, Kelso

Owner: Historic Scotland   **Contact:** The Custodian

Set on a high rocky knoll this well preserved 16th century tower houses an exhibition of tapestries and costume dolls depicting characters from Sir Walter Scott's *Minstrelsy of the Scottish Borders.*

Location: OS Ref. NT638 347. Nr Smailholm Village, 6m W of Kelso on B6937.

Opening Times: 1 Apr - 30 Sept: Mon - Sat 9.30am - 6.30pm, Sun 2 - 6.30pm. Last ticket 6pm.

Admission: Adult £1.50, Conc. £1, Child 75p.

SORN CASTLE

Tel: 01292 268181

Ayrshire KA5 6HR

Owner: Mrs R G McIntyre   **Contact:** Mrs R G McIntyre

Originally 14th century castle. James V visited the castle then owned by the Earl of Winton in 1598. The castle has been enlarged several times, most recently in 1908.

Location: OS Ref. NS555 265. 4m E of Mauchline on B743.

Opening Times: By appointment.

Grounds suitable.   Compulsory.   In grounds, on leads.

SOUTER JOHNNIE'S COTTAGE

Tel: 01655 760603

Main Road, Kirkoswald KA19 8HY

Owner: The National Trust for Scotland   **Contact:** Ms Jan Gibson

The home of John Davidson, original 'Souter' (cobbler) of Robert Burns' famous narrative poem *Tam O' Shanter.* Burns mementos and restored cobbler's workshop. Life-sized stone figures in adjacent 'ale-house'.

Location: OS Ref. NS240 070. On A77, in Kirkoswald village, 4m SW of Maybole.

Opening Times: Good Fri - 30 Sept: daily 11.30 - 5pm. Weekends in Oct: 11.30 - 5pm (last admission 4.30pm).

Admission: Adult £1.80, Child £1.20, Family £4.80. Groups: Adult £1.50, School £1.

House suitable.   **P** Limited.   No dogs.

SWEETHEART ABBEY

Tel: 01387 785397

New Abbey Village

Owner: Historic Scotland **Contact:** The Custodian

Cistercian abbey founded in 1273 by Devorgilla, in memory of her husband John Balliol. The principal feature is the well preserved precinct wall enclosing 30 acres. She also founded Balliol College, Oxford.

Location: OS Ref. NX965 663. In New Abbey Village, on A710 8m S of Dumfries.

Opening Times: 1 Apr - 30 Sept: Mon - Sat 9.30am - 6.30pm, Sun 2 - 6.30pm. Last ticket 6pm. 1 Oct - 31 Mar: Mon - Wed & Sat 9.30am - 4.30pm, Thur 9.30am - 12 noon, Fri closed, Sun 2 - 4.30pm. Last ticket 4pm.

Admission: Adult £1, Conc. 50p, Child 50p. Joint entry ticket with New Abbey Corn Mill: Adult £2.80, Conc. £1.75, Child £1.25.

THIRLESTANE CASTLE

THIRLESTANE, CASTLE LAUDER, BERWICKSHIRE TD2 6RU

Owner: Thirlestane Castle Trust *Contact: Peter Jarvis*

Tel: 01578 722430 **Fax:** 01578 722761

One of Scotland's oldest and finest castles standing in lovely Border countryside. Thirlestane was the seat of the Earls and Duke of Lauderdale and is still home to the Maitland family. Unsurpassed 17th century ceilings, fine portrait collection, large collection of historic toys, country life exhibitions. Woodland walks. STB commended. MGC Registered. State rooms available for functions.

Location: OS Ref. NT540 473. Off A68 at Lauder, 28m S of Edinburgh.

Opening Times: Easter week then 1 May - 30 Sept. May, Jun & Sept: Sun, Mon, Wed & Thur. Jul & Aug: daily except Sat. Castle: 2 - 5pm. Grounds: 12 - 6pm. Last admission 4.30pm.

Admission: Adult £4, Family £10. Groups £3pp. Grounds only £1.

i Shop. Tearoom. By arrangement. In grounds, on leads.

THREAVE CASTLE

Tel: 01831 168512

Castle Douglas

Owner: The National Trust for Scotland **Contact:** Historic Scotland

Built by Archibald the Grim in the late 14th century, early stronghold of the Black Douglases. Round its base is an artillery fortification built before 1455 when the castle was besieged by James II. Ring the bell and the custodian will come to ferry you over. Long walk to property. Owned by The National Trust for Scotland but under the guardianship of Historic Scotland.

Location: OS Ref. NX739 623. 2m W of Castle Douglas on the A75.

Opening Times: 1 Apr - 30 Sept: Mon - Sat 9.30am - 6.30pm, Sun 2 - 6.30pm. Last ticket 6pm.

Admission: Adult £1.50, Conc. £1, Child 75p. Charges include ferry trip.

THREAVE GARDEN

Tel: 01556 502575

Castle Douglas DG7 1RX

Owner: The National Trust for Scotland **Contact:** Trevor Jones

The garden has a wide range of features and a good collection of plants. There are peat and woodland garden plants and a colourful rock garden. Summer months bring a superb show from the herbaceous beds and borders. The heather gardens give a splash of colour, along with bright berries in the autumn. Truly a garden for all seasons.

Location: OS Ref. NX752 605. Off A75, 1m SW of Castle Douglas.

Opening Times: Estate & garden: All year, daily 9.30am - sunset. Walled garden and glasshouses: all year 9.30am - 5pm. Visitor Centre, Exhibition, & Shop: 28 Mar - 31 Oct: daily, 9.30am - 5.30pm. Restaurant: 10am - 5pm.

Admission: Adult £3.70, Child £2.50. Groups: Adult £3, School £1. Family £9.90.

i Shop. Grounds suitable. WC. Restaurant.

TRAQUAIR HOUSE

See page 51 for full page entry.

WHITHORN PRIORY

Tel: 01988 500508

Whithorn

Owner: Historic Scotland **Contact:** The Project Manager

Part of the 'Whithorn Cradle of Christianity' attraction. The site of the first Christian church in Scotland. Founded as 'Candida Casa' by St Ninian in the early 5th century it later became the cathedral church of Galloway. In the museum is a fine collection of early Christian stones including the Monreith Cross. Visitor Centre and archaeological dig.

Location: OS Ref. NX445 403. At Whithorn on the A746.

Opening Times: Please telephone 01988 500700 for details.

Admission: Joint ticket by Whithorn Trust gives entry to Priory, Priory Museum and archaeological dig.

Thirlestane Castle, Berwickshire.

Duart Castle, Isle of Mull (West Highlands and Islands).

INVERARAY CASTLE
Inveraray

The Duke of Argyll's family have lived in Inveraray since the early 15th century. The present Castle was built between 1740 and 1790.

The ancient Royal Burgh of Inveraray lies about 60 miles north west of Glasgow by Loch Fyne in an area of spectacular natural beauty combining the ruggedness of highland scenery with the sheltered tidal loch 90 miles from the open sea.

The Castle is the home of the Duke and Duchess of Argyll. Its fairytale exterior belies the grandeur of its gracious interior. The building was designed by Roger Morris and decorated by Robert Mylne, the clerk of works being William Adam, father of Robert and John, who did much of the laying out of the present Royal Burgh, an unrivalled example of an early planned town.

Visitors may see the famous Armoury Hall containing some 1300 pieces, French tapestries made especially for the Castle, fine examples of Scottish, English and French furniture together with a wealth of other works of art including china, silver and family artifacts, all of which form a unique collection spanning the generations which are identified by a magnificent genealogical display in the Clan Room.

CONTACT

The Factor
Dept HHD
Argyll Estates Office
Cherry Park
Inveraray
Argyll
PA32 8XE

Tel: (01499) 302203

Fax: (01499) 302421

LOCATION

OS Ref. NN100 090

From Edinburgh $2^{1}/_{2}$ - 3 hrs via Glasgow.

Just NE of Inveraray on A83. W shore of Loch Fyne.

Bus: Bus route stopping point within $^{1}/_{2}$ m.

OPENING TIMES

SUMMER

5 April - 12 October

April, May, June, September & October:
Mon, Tue, Wed, Thur & Sat:
10am - 1pm & 2 - 5.45pm
Fri: Closed
Sun: 1 - 5.45pm.

July - August
daily: 10am - 5.45pm
(including Friday)
Sun: 1 - 5.45pm.

Last admissions
12.30 & 5pm.

ADMISSION

SUMMER
House only

Adult £4.00
Child (under 16yrs)......£2.00
OAP.........................£3.00
Family (2+2) £10.00
Groups (min. 20)
20% Discount

WINTER
Closed

---

i Shop. No photography. Guide books in French, Italian, Japanese and German translations.

Visitors may alight at the entrance to the castle before parking. Wheelchair ramp to Castle plus two steps. All main public rooms suitable but two long flights of stairs to the smaller rooms upstairs. WCs.

Tearoom, seats up to 50. Menus available on request. Groups book in advance. Tel: (01786) 813317.

Available for up to 100 people at no additional cost. Groups please book in advance. Tour time: 1 hr.

P 100 cars. Separate coach park close to Castle

Welcome. £1.50 per child. A guide can be provided. Areas of interest include a nature walk.

No dogs.

ACHAMORE GARDENS

Tel: 01583 505254 / 505267

Isle of Gigha, Argyll PA41 7AD

Owner: Mr and Mrs Derek Holt **Contact:** Mr William Howden
Gardens only open. Sub-tropical gardens created by Sir James Horlick who bought Gigha in 1944.

Location: OS Ref. NR650 500. Off the Mull of Kintyre. Ferry from Tayinloan.

Opening Times: Dawn until dusk every day.

Admission: Adult £2, Child £1.

Grounds suitable.   Ample.   In grounds, on leads.

ARDANAISEIG GARDENS

Tel: 01866 833333 **Fax:** 01866 833222

Oban, Argyll PA35 1HE

Owner: S B Gray **Contact:** Robert Francis
Woodland garden with fine trees and a great variety of rhododendrons, azaleas and other flowering shrubs surrounding one acre walled garden with large herbaceous border.

Location: OS Ref. NN090 240. 9m S of Taynuilt on B845 then 3m E from Kilchrenan.

Opening Times: All year: 9am - 9pm.

Admission: Adult £2, Child free.

Ground floor & grounds suitable.   Licensed restaurant.   In grounds, on leads.

ARDCHATTAN PRIORY

Tel: 01631 750274

Oban, Argyll PA37 1RQ

Owner: Mrs Sarah Hope Troughton **Contact:** Lt Col R Campbell Preston
The oldest inhabited house in Scotland. 3 acre garden, wild garden to west of house, formal garden in front, two herbaceous borders, 3 shrub borders, rose garden. Fine variety of shrubs, trees and roses.

Location: OS Ref. NM971 349. 5m E Connel Bridge, north side.

Opening Times: 1 Apr - 31 Oct: Dawn - dusk (9am - 9pm).

Admission: Adult £1, Child free, OAP £1. (Charges may vary from May - Aug).

Shop.   Available.

ARDUAINE GARDEN

Glyn Satterley

ARDUAINE, BY OBAN, ARGYLL PA34 4XQ

Owner: The National Trust for Scotland *Contact:* Maurice Wilkins

Tel: 01852 200366

A haven of tranquillity nestling on the west coast, Arduaine Garden is most spectacular in the late spring and early summer when the rhododendrons and azaleas are at their glorious best. With informal perennial borders giving a delightful display of colour throughout the season, the garden offers pleasant surroundings for a relaxing walk through the woodland garden to the coastal viewpoint, or simply an opportunity to sit and enjoy the peaceful atmosphere of the water garden.

Location: OS Ref. NM798 105. On A816, 20m S of Oban and 17m N of Lochgilphead.

Opening Times: All year: daily 9.30am - sunset.

Admission: Adult £2.30, Child £1.50, Family £6.10. Groups: Adult £1.80. School £1.

By arrangement.   Ample.   Guide dogs only.

BALLOCH CASTLE COUNTRY PARK

BALLOCH, DUNBARTONSHIRE G83 8LX

Contact: Loch Lomond Park Authority Ranger Service

Tel: 01389 758216 **Fax:** 01389 755721

Balloch Castle is a 200 acre country park situated on the bonnie banks of Loch Lomond. One of the finest parks in the whole of the country, it is steeped in history and offers breathtaking views of superb scenery. This ancient seat of the Lennox offers the visitor a chance to blend the wild, natural beauty of Scotland with the formal glory of the ornamental gardens and splendid trees of former estate days. Balloch Castle, now the Visitor Centre, was built in 1808 to be in the 'castle-gothic' style of architecture and was one of the first of its type built in Scotland.

Location: OS Ref. NS390 830. SE shore of Loch Lomond, off A82 for Balloch or A811 for Stirling.

Opening Times: Visitor Centre: Apr - Oct: daily, 10am - 6pm. Country Park: All year, dawn - dusk.

Admission: Free for both visitor centre and country park.

BANNOCKBURN HERITAGE CENTRE

Tel: 01786 812664

Glasgow Road, Stirling FK7 0IJ

Owner: The National Trust for Scotland **Contact:** Judith Fairley
From this battlefield the Scots 'sent them homeward to think again', when Edward II's English army was soundly defeated by King Robert the Bruce. Inside the Heritage Centre there is a life-size statue of William Wallace, Bruce on his throne, a display enriched with replicas, vignettes of Scottish life and a panorama of historical characters.

Location: OS Ref. NS810 910. Off M80 & M9/J9, 2m S of Stirling.

Opening Times: Site: All year: daily. Heritage Centre & Shop: 1 - 31 Mar and 1 Nov - 23 Dec: daily 11am - 3pm. 1 Apr - 31 Oct: daily 10am - 5.30pm (last visual show ½ hr before closing). Shop closed 1 - 10 Nov for stocktaking.

Admission: Adult £2.30, Child £1.50, Family £6.10. Groups: Adult £1.80, School £1.

Shop.   Suitable. WC.   Ample.   In grounds, on leads.

BONAWE IRON FURNACE

Tel: 01866 822432

Taynuilt, Argyll

Owner: Historic Scotland **Contact:** The Custodian
Founded in 1753 by Cumbrian iron masters this is the most complete remaining charcoal fuelled ironworks in Britain. Displays show how iron was once made here.

Location: OS Ref. NN005 310. By the village of Taynuilt off the A85.

Opening Times: 1 Apr - 30 Sept: Mon - Sat, 9.30am - 6.30pm, Sun, 2 - 6.30pm. Last ticket 6pm.

Admission: Adult £2.30, Conc. £1.50, Child £1.

CALLENDAR HOUSE

CALLENDAR PARK, FALKIRK FK1 1YR

Owner: *Falkirk Council*   **Contact:** *Mrs M. McFeat*

Tel: 01324 503770   **Fax:** 01324 503771

Imposing mansion set in attractive parkland with a 900 year history. Facilities include a working kitchen of 1825 where costumed interpreters carry out daily chores including cooking based on 1820s recipes. Exhibition area, 'Story of Callendar House' plus two contemporary galleries with regularly changing exhibitions. There is also a history research centre and Georgian Teashop at the Stables.

Location: OS Ref. NS898 794. E of Falkirk town centre on Callendar Rd (A803).

Opening Times: All year: Mon - Sat, 10am - 5pm also Suns & BH's, Apr - Sept: 2 - 5 pm. Last admission 4.15pm.

Admission: Adult £1.65, OAP/Child 85p.

i Gift shop.   Suitable.   Tearoom.   Guide dogs only.

SPECIAL EVENTS

DEC: Christmas at Callendar House, seasonal recipes from the 1825 kitchen including spit roasting a goose.

DUART CASTLE

ISLE OF MULL, ARGYLL PA64 6AP

Owner: *Sir Lachlan Maclean Bt*   **Contact:** *Sir Lachlan Maclean Bt*

Tel: 01680 812309 **Fax:** 01577 830311

Duart Castle has been a Maclean stronghold since the 12th century. The keep was built by Lachlan Lubanach, 5th Chief, in 1360. Burnt by the English in 1758, the castle was restored in 1912 and today is still the home of the Chief of the Clan Maclean. It has a spectacular position overlooking the Sound of Mull.

Location: OS Ref. NM750 350. Off A849 on the east point of the Isle of Mull.

Opening Times: 1 May - 14 Oct: 10.30am - 6pm.

Admission: Adult £3.30, Child £1.65, OAP £2.20, Student £2.75, Family £8.25.

i Shop.   Not suitable.   Tearoom.   In grounds, on leads.

CASTLE CAMPBELL   **Tel:** 01259 742408

Dollar Glen, Central District

Owner: The National Trust for Scotland   **Contact:** Historic Scotland

Known as 'Castle Gloom' this spectacularly sited 15th century fortress was the lowland stronghold of the Campbells. Stunning views from the parapet walk. Owned by The National Trust for Scotland but under the guardianship of Historic Scotland.

Location: OS Ref. NS961 993. At head of Dollar Glen, 10m E of Stirling on the A91.

Opening Times: 1 Apr - 30 Sept: Mon - Sat 9.30am - 6.30pm, Sun 2 - 6.30pm. Last ticket 6pm. 1 Oct - 31 Mar: Mon - Sat 9.30am - 4.30pm (closed Thur pm & Fri all day) Sun 2 - 4.30pm. Last ticket 4pm.

Admission: Adult £2.30, Conc. £1.50, Child £1.

DOUNE CASTLE    **Tel:** 01786 841742

Doune

Owner: Earl of Moray (leased to Historic Scotland)   **Contact:** The Custodian

The formidable 14th century courtyard castle was built for the Regent Albany. The striking keep-gatehouse also combines domestic quarters including the splendid Lord's Hall with its carved oak screen, musicians' gallery and double fireplace.

Location: OS Ref. NN720 020. In Doune, 8m S of Callendar on the A84.

Opening Times: 1 Apr - 30 Sept: Mon - Sat, 9.30am - 6.30pm, Sun 2 - 6.30pm. 1 Oct - 31 Mar: Mon - Wed & Sat 9.30am - 4.30pm, Thur 9.30am - 12 noon, Fri closed, Sun 2 - 4.30pm. Last admission $^1/_2$ hr before closing.

Admission: Adult £2.30, Child £1, Conc. £1.50.

DUMBARTON CASTLE   **Tel:** 01389 732167

Dumbarton, Strathclyde

Owner: Historic Scotland   **Contact:** The Custodian

Location: OS Ref. NS401 744. In Dumbarton on the A82.

Opening Times: 1 Apr - 30 Sept: Mon - Sat 9.30am - 6.30pm, Sun 2 - 6.30pm. Last ticket 6pm. 1 Oct - 31 Mar: Mon - Wed & Sat 9.30am - 4.30pm, Thur 9.30am - 12 noon, Fri Closed, Sun 2 - 4.30pm. Last ticket 4pm.

Admission: Adult £1.50, Conc. £1, Child 75p.

DUNBLANE CATHEDRAL   **Tel:** 01786 823388

Dunblane

Owner: Historic Scotland   **Contact:** The Custodian

One of Scotland's noblest medieval churches. The lower part of the tower is Romanesque but the larger part of the building is of the 13th century. It was restored in 1889 - 93 by Sir Rowand Anderson.

Location: OS Ref. NN782 015. In Dunblane.

Admission: Free.

DUNSTAFFNAGE CASTLE & CHAPEL   **Tel:** 01631 562465

Oban, Argyll

Owner: Historic Scotland   **Contact:** The Custodian

A very fine 13th century castle built on a rock with a great curtain wall. Close by are the remains of a chapel with beautiful architectural detail.

Location: OS Ref. NM883 345. $3^1/_2$ m from Oban off the A85.

Opening Times: 1 Apr - 30 Sept: Mon - Sat 9.30am - 6.30pm, Sun 2 - 6.30pm. Last ticket 6pm.

Admission: Adult £1.50, Conc. £1, Child 75p.

GLENCOE

BALLACHULISH, ARGYLL PA39 4HX

Owner: The National Trust for Scotland   *Contact: Derrick Warner*

Tel: 01855 811307 or 811729 (during closed season) **Fax:** 01855 811772

This is a breathtaking, dramatic glen with jagged peaks incised on either side by cascading water. In 1692 many of the MacDonald clan were massacred by soldiers of King William's army, to whom they had given hospitality. Wildlife abounds and herds of red deer, wildcat and golden eagle enjoy this wilderness area.

Location: OS Ref. NN100 590. Off A82, 17m S of Fort William.

Opening Times: Site: All year, daily. Visitor Centre & Snack Bar: 28 Mar - 18 May and 1 Sept - 31 Oct: daily, 10am - 5pm. 19 May - 31 Aug: daily, 9.30am - 5.30pm, Last admission 1/2 hr before closing.

Admission: Adult 50p, Child 30p.

 Shop.   Ground floor suitable. WC.   Kiosk. Guide dogs only.

INCHMAHOME PRIORY

Tel: 01877 385294

Port of Menteith

Owner: Historic Scotland   **Contact:** The Custodian

A beautifully situated Augustinian priory on an island in the Lake of Menteith founded in 1238 with much of the building surviving. The five year old Mary Queen of Scots was sent here for safety in 1547.

Location: OS Ref. NN574 005. On an island in Lake of Menteith. Reached by ferry from Port of Menteith, 4m E of Aberfoyle off A81.

Opening Times: 1 Apr - 30 Sept: Mon - Sat 9.30am - 6.30pm, Sun 2 - 6.30pm. Last ticket 6pm.

Admission: Adult £2.80, Conc. £1.80, Child £1. Charge includes ferry trip.

INVERARAY CASTLE

See page 59 for full page entry.

INVERARAY JAIL

Tel: 01499 302381 **Fax:** 01499 302195

Church Square, Inveraray, Argyll PA32 8TX

Owner: Visitor Centres Ltd   **Contact:** J Linley

A living 19th century prison! Uniformed prisoners and warders, life-like figures, imaginative exhibitions, sounds, smells and trials in progress, bring the 1820 courtroom and former county prison back to life. New exhibition now open. A comparison of life 'In Prison Today'.

Location: OS Ref. NN100 090. Church Square, Inveraray, Argyll.

Opening Times: Apr - Oct: 9.30am - 6pm, last admission 5pm. Nov - Mar: 10am - 5pm, last admission 4pm.

Admission: Adult £4.20, Child £2.10, OAP £2.65, Family £11.50. Groups: £3.40, OAP £2.15.

KILCHURN CASTLE

Tel: 0131 668 8800 **Ferry Info:** 01838 200440/9

Loch Awe, Nr Dalmally, Argyll

Owner: Historic Scotland   **Contact:** The Custodian

A square tower built by Sir Colin Campbell of Glenorchy c1550. It was much enlarged in 1693 to give the building, now a ruin, its present picturesque outline. Spectacular views of Loch Awe.

Location: OS Ref. NN133 276. At the NE end of Loch Awe, 1 1/2 m W of Dalmally.

Opening Times: All year, but check ferry times.

Admission: Free.

THE HILL HOUSE

UPPER COLQUHOUN STREET, HELENSBURGH G84 9AJ

Owner: The National Trust for Scotland   *Contact: Mrs Annie Ellis*

Tel: 01436 673900

Certainly the finest domestic creation of the famous Scottish architect and artist, Charles Rennie Mackintosh. He set this 20th century masterpiece high on a hillside overlooking the Firth of Clyde. Mackintosh also designed furniture, fittings and decorative schemes to complement the house, and suggested a layout for the garden which has been renovated by the Trust.

Location: OS Ref. NS300 820. Off B832, between A82 & A814, 23m NW of Glasgow.

Opening Times: Good Fri - 31 Oct; daily, 1.30 - 5.30pm, last admission 5pm. Tearoom: 1.30 - 4.30pm. Increasing visitor numbers are placing great strain on the structure of The Hill House, which was designed for domestic purposes. Access may be restricted at peak times.

Admission: Adult £4.50, Child £3, Family £12. Groups: Adult £3.60, School £1.

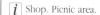 Tearoom.

MOUNT STUART HOUSE & GARDEN

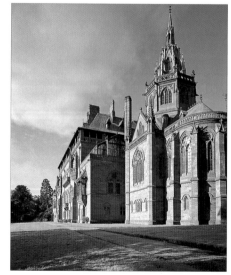

ISLE OF BUTE PA20 9LR

Owner: The Mount Stuart Trust *Contact: The Administrator*

Tel: 01700 503877 **Fax:** 01700 505313

Spectacular High Victorian gothic house, ancestral home of the Marquesses of Bute. Splendid interiors, art collection and architectural detail. Set in 300 acres of stunning woodlands, mature Victorian pinetum, arboretum and exotic gardens. Countryside Ranger Service. Scottish Tourism Oscar winner 1995.

Location: OS Ref. NS100 600. 5m S of Rothesay Pierhead, local bus service to house. Frequent ferry service from Wemyss Bay, Renfrewshire & Colintraive, Argyll. 1 hr from Glasgow Airport.

Opening Times: 19/20 & 26/27 April, also 2 May - 12 Oct: daily except Tue & Thur. Gardens: 10am - 5pm. House: 11am - 5pm. Last admission 4.30pm.

Admission: House & Gardens: Adult £5.50, Child £2.50, Family £15. Gardens: Adult £3, Child £2, Family £8. Conc. & group rates given. Pre-booked guided tours available.

 Shop. Picnic area.   Suitable. WC.   Tearoom. No dogs.

ROTHESAY CASTLE

Tel: 01700 502691

Rothesay, Isle of Bute

Owner: Historic Scotland   **Contact:** The Custodian

A favourite residence of the Stuart Kings, this is a wonderful example of a 13th century circular castle of enclosure with 16th century forework containing the Great Hall. Attacked by Vikings in its earlier days.

Location: OS Ref. NS088 646. In Rothesay, Isle of Bute. Ferry from Wemyss Bay on the A78.

Opening Times: 1 Apr - 30 Sept: Mon - Sat 9.30am - 6.30pm, Sun 2 - 6.30pm. Last ticket 6pm. 1 Oct - 31 Mar: Mon - Wed & Sat 9.30am - 4.30pm, Thur 9.30am - 12 noon, Fri closed, Sun 2 - 4.30pm. Last ticket 4pm..

Admission: Adult £1.50, Conc. £1, Child 75p.

STIRLING CASTLE

Tel: 01786 450000

Stirling

Owner: Historic Scotland   **Contact:** The Administrator

Considered by many as the grandest of all Scotland's castles with strong links to Mary Queen of Scots. She was crowned in the chapel in 1543 and narrowly escaped death by fire in 1561.

Location: OS Ref. NS790 941. At the head of Stirling's historic old town off the M9.

Opening Times: 1 Apr - 30 Sept: daily 9.30am - 6pm. Last ticket 5.15pm. 1 Oct - 31 Mar: daily 9.30am - 5pm. Last ticket 4.15pm.

Admission: Adult £4, Conc. £2.50, Child (under 16) £1.20. Parking up to 3 hrs: cars £2, coaches £5.

TOROSAY CASTLE & GARDENS

CRAIGNURE, ISLE OF MULL PA65 6AY

Owner: *Mr Chris James*   ***Contact:*** *Mrs Dee Hay*

Tel: 01680 812421 **Fax:** 01680 812470

Torosay Castle and Gardens set on the magnificent Island of Mull, was completed in 1858 by the eminent architect David Bryce in the Scottish baronial style, and is surrounded by 12 acres of spectacular gardens which offer an exciting contrast between formal terraces, impressive statue walk and informal woodland, also rhododendron collection, alpine, walled, bog and Japanese gardens. The house offers family history, portraits, scrapbooks and antiques in an informal and relaxed atmosphere.

Location: OS Ref. NM730 350. $1^1/2$ m SE of Craignure by A849. 2m W of Duart Castle.

Opening Times: House: Easter - Oct: Mon - Sun, 10.30am - 5.30pm, last admission 5pm. Gardens: all year, daily during daylight hours.

Admission: Adult £4.50, Child £1.50, Conc. £3.50. Groups: Adult £3.50, Child £1, Conc. £3.50.

i Shop.   Grounds suitable. WC.   Tearoom.   In grounds, on leads.

YOUNGER BOTANIC GARDEN BENMORE

Tel: 01369 706261

Dunoon, Argyll PA23 8QU

Fax: 01369 706369

Contact: The Curator

A botanical paradise. Enter the magnificent avenue of giant redwood and follow trails through the formal garden and hillside woodlands to a viewpoint with its spectacular outlook over the Holy Loch and the Eachaig Valley. World famous collections of rhododendrons and conifers.

Location: OS Ref. NS150 850. 7m N of Dunoon on A815.

Opening Times: 15 Mar - 31 Oct: daily, 10am - 6pm.

Admission: Adult £2, Child 50p, Conc. £1.50, Family £4.50. Group discounts available.

i Shop & plant centre. Conferences.   Grounds suitable. WC.   Licensed Kiosk.   By arrangement.   P Ample.   In grounds, on leads.

Inverary Castle, Argyll (West Highlands and Islands).